Richard Sadleir PhD

Animals of
Australia
& New Zealand

illustrated by A. Oxenham

Hamlyn · London
Sun Books · Melbourne

FOREWORD

Australia and New Zealand and their adjoining islands, long separated from the other continents, form a fascinating zoogeographical region. Though they are often automatically linked together in the minds of people on the other side of the world, they are of course very different in their native animal life. Australia is the home of the monotremes, the most primitive mammals, and of a variety of marsupial forms, from the tiny Honey Possum to the celebrated kangaroos, and it has a rich and varied bird life. New Zealand is remarkable for the gaps in its fauna. There are only two native mammals, both bats, and the birds, having evolved in the absence of predators, tend to be terrestrial.

Both countries are now inhabited by numerous foreign species. Most were introduced deliberately – the others are the scavenging rats and mice that follow man wherever he goes. New Zealand especially faces an enormous ecological problem.

No book this size could hope to cover in detail the animal life of this region. What we have done is to describe and illustrate some of the most interesting and attractive animals in the hope of stimulating further interest.

In this book the common names of species are capitalized (such as Common Brown Snake, Great Grey Kangaroo) to distinguish them from the names of groups of animals (such as snakes, kangaroos).

Published by The Hamlyn Publishing Group Limited
London · New York · Sydney · Toronto
Hamlyn House, Feltham, Middlesex, England
In association with Sun Books Pty Ltd. Melbourne.
Copyright © The Hamlyn Publishing Group Limited 1970
SBN 600 00090 7
Photoset by BAS Printers Limited, Wallop, Hampshire
Colour separations by Schwitter Limited, Zurich
Printed in England by Sir Joseph Causton & Sons Limited

CONTENTS

HERALDIC ANIMALS OF AUSTRALIA AND NEW ZEALAND

It is to be expected that Australia and New Zealand, with their unique animal life, should come to be symbolized in the minds of people the world over by some of their more remarkable species.

The coat of arms of the Commonwealth of Australia includes in heraldic fashion a number of that country's interesting animals. The shield is supported by two of the continent's most representative animals, a kangaroo for the mammals and the Emu for the birds. Two States have animals on their individual shields which are incorporated in the Commonwealth arms. South Australia has a heraldically modified magpie and Western Australia has the Black Swan. The only non-Australian animal depicted is the heraldic Lion representing Tasmania.

The kiwi is commonly thought of as representing New Zealand. It does not appear on the country's coat of arms but frequently appears on postage stamps and coins.

White-backed Magpie

Black Swan

Great Grey Kangaroo

Emu

THE AUSTRALASIAN REGION

Australia, together with New Zealand, New Guinea and adjacent smaller islands, forms one of the world's major zoogeographic regions. How the flora and fauna of the region arrived originally is much debated among biologists. One school believes that most of the plants and animals originated from basic stock found millions of years ago in the postulated super-continent of Gondwanaland which split into several land masses that drifted apart to form the present Antarctica, Australia, southern Africa and South America, and that the basic biological elements were carried with them and evolved into the characteristic flora and fauna seen today.

A second school of thought emphasizes the similarity with fossil forms of Asia and suggests that there was once, or per-

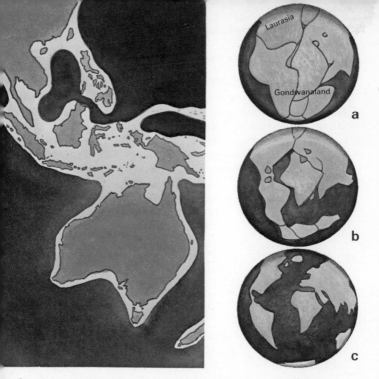

One theory holds that the ancestors of Australia's flora and fauna spread over a land bridge (*left*) from South-east Asia. Another is that the flora and fauna developed from those of (a) Gondwanaland which (b) split apart to form (c) the present southern continents.

haps many times, a land bridge to South-east Asia over which the plants and animals spread. It is possible that both schools are correct, and that the land bridge existed after the continent of Australia had drifted from Gondwanaland.

The origin of the New Zealand flora and fauna is even more shrouded in mystery, and the question of a land bridge between Australia and New Zealand is still a source of controversy. The New Zealand fauna shows similarities to that of New Caledonia and New Guinea, but the fascinating distribution of one genus of trees, the southern beech (*Nothofagus* species), in New Zealand and South America, and in the fossil record of Antarctica, suggests a common connection.

Australian climate

Australia's climate is largely governed by its relatively flat topography and the size of its continental land mass. These features, combined with its latitude, control the dominant feature of the climate, the pattern of rainfall. Most of the rain falls on coastal areas subject to varying onshore rain-bearing winds. In summer the low pressure belt over the northern part of the continent results in monsoonal winds and rain which extend somewhat down the eastern side of Queensland. In winter the southern regions receive rain from westerly winds. Over most of Australia, however, the rainfall is less than twenty inches a year and this small amount is ineffective in many areas because of the high rate of evaporation.

Climate

ARID
SEMI-ARID
TROPICAL
MEDITERRANEAN
TEMPERATE

Temperature regions in Australia show a fairly regular north-south progression. The combination of temperature and rainfall patterns results in the fairly clear delineation of Australian climate zones. The central area is either arid or semi-arid and characterized by infrequent, irregular and light rainfalls. To the north a more tropical climate exists with hot wet summers and warm dry winters. This climate extends down the eastern coast. In the south of the continent, both the west and east sides have the characteristic cool wet winters and hot dry summers of a Mediterranean climate, but in the eastern areas this is modified as the rainfall is more evenly spread over the year. In the far south, Tasmania is cooler with a heavier annual rainfall falling mainly in winter.

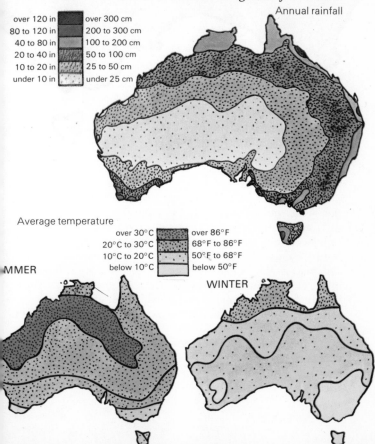

Annual rainfall

over 120 in — over 300 cm
80 to 120 in — 200 to 300 cm
40 to 80 in — 100 to 200 cm
20 to 40 in — 50 to 100 cm
10 to 20 in — 25 to 50 cm
under 10 in — under 25 cm

Average temperature

over 30°C — over 86°F
20°C to 30°C — 68°F to 86°F
10°C to 20°C — 50°F to 68°F
below 10°C — below 50°F

SUMMER

WINTER

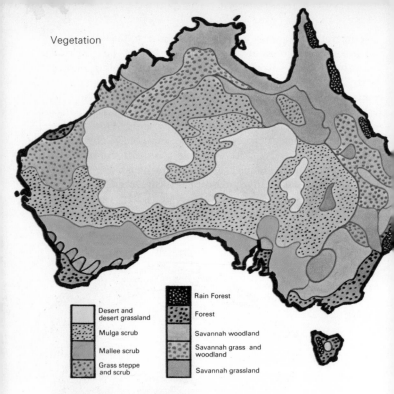

Desert and desert grassland

Mulga scrub

Mallee scrub

Grass steppe and scrub

Rain Forest

Forest

Savannah woodland

Savannah grass and woodland

Savannah grassland

Australian vegetation

The dominant factor controlling the distribution of vegetation is the amount of rainfall. The central part of the continent is a desert with only a few spindly trees along the dried-up water-courses; the dominant plants are patches of tough-leaved hummocky grasses like spinifex. To the north, south and east, as the rainfall increases, this gives way to various types of savannah, progressing through grassland to shrub savannah and woodland savannah. The grasses are of a softer type and the trees, although thin and with few leaves, are more evenly distributed across the landscape. Farther north the tree cover becomes more dense and an underlayer of shrubs develops.

To the south of the savannah regions occur two typically Australian types of vegetation. The mulga scrubland is

Desert

Eucalypt forest

Mulga scrub

Tropical forest

dominated by the thin scraggly Mulga (*Acacia aneura*). The widespread mallee scrub is characterized by various species of *Eucalyptus*. As the rainfall continues to increase to the south-west and east, a more dense eucalypt hard-leaved tree woodland develops, and trees such as jarrah, redgum, marree stringybark start to form true forested areas. Where the rainfall becomes really heavy, these trees give way to the beautiful tall forests of bluegum, mountain ash, karri and many other large species of forest eucalypts. Finally there are two other main vegetation types. In the mountainous areas of the south-east is found an alpine complex of heath, tussock grass and snow gum, while on the north-east coast are patches of a monsoon type of forest of very dense semitropical vegetation with thick undergrowth, vines and epiphytes.

New Zealand climate and vegetation

New Zealand is too small a country to suffer the extremes of climate found in the great continents. It has an oceanic climate similar to that of Britain, sea winds keeping the land cool in summer and mild in winter.

The North Island is warmer than the South Island, as a comparison of temperature figures for Auckland (in the North Island) and Dunedin (South Island) show. The average January temperature in Auckland is about 67°F and in Dunedin 58°F. In July, the temperatures are 52°F and 42°F respectively. Frost seldom occurs in low regions in the north. In winter, the warm East Australian current gives the west coast of New Zealand a warmer climate than the east coast, but in summer, the westerly winds warm up as they pass over the land, making the east hotter than the west.

The westerlies bring a heavy rainfall of 100 to 200 inches a year to the mountainous west coast of the South Island, and snow falls deeply on the Southern Alps. But the eastern half of the South Island, lying in the lee of these mountains, gets only 20 to 30 inches each year, falling mainly in the summer. Rainfall in the North Island lies between these two extremes at 40 to 70 inches a year. It is evenly distributed over the whole of the Island, and no dry or wet seasons occur.

When the Maoris came to New Zealand, they found a land clothed in rich forests inhabited by a few birds. Forests of pines, firs, and beech, and in the wet regions, a dense and luxuriant rain forest of evergreen trees, shrubs and bushes jostling with great tree ferns and creepers, now cover a fifth of the land. But whatever its nature, the forest is known to New Zealanders as 'the bush'. The whole of the North Island was forested originally, and at Waipoua, there is still a great forest of kauri pines, which yield a good timber and a fossilized gum used to make polish and varnish. New Zealand flax (*Phormium*) grows in the wetter regions, especially in the northern Auckland Peninsula, yielding a useful fibre. In the cooler South Island, beech forests cover lower mountain slopes, with conifers reaching up to the snow line. Over the dry eastern plains grow scrub forests of manuka, a tree of the myrtle family, and great areas of tussock grass used to graze sheep.

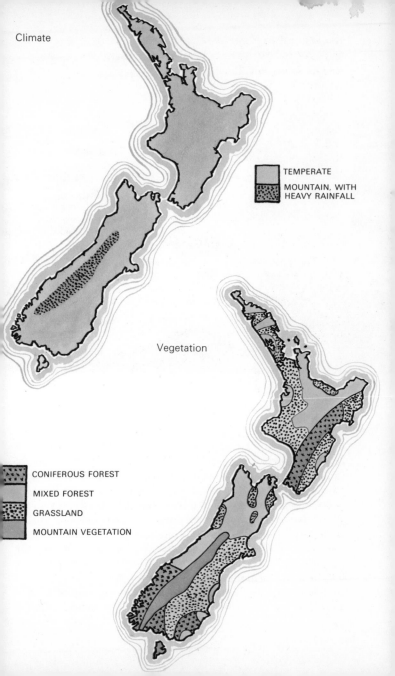

Climate

TEMPERATE

MOUNTAIN, WITH
HEAVY RAINFALL

Vegetation

CONIFEROUS FOREST

MIXED FOREST

GRASSLAND

MOUNTAIN VEGETATION

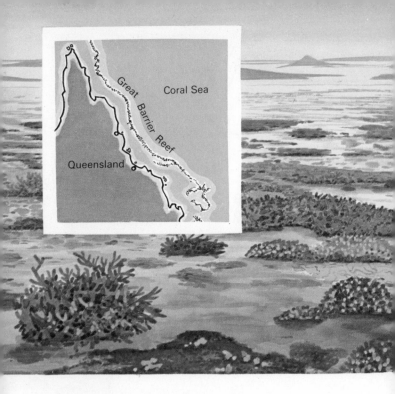

THE GREAT BARRIER REEF

Probably the greatest single structure made by living organisms is the Great Barrier Reef situated off the eastern coast of Queensland. It is over 1,250 miles long, hundreds of fathoms deep, and its width ranges from a few hundred yards to several miles in places. This enormous edifice was constructed by millions of minute animals, the coral polyps. They live in continuous colonies of closely packed individual polyps, and reproduce by budding of new members from the older individuals. Coral polyps are members of the phylum Coelenterata – the same group which contains the jellyfish, sea anemones and sea cucumbers. The living animals secrete a very hard and durable external skeleton of a limestone-like nature which remains, after the animals die, to

14

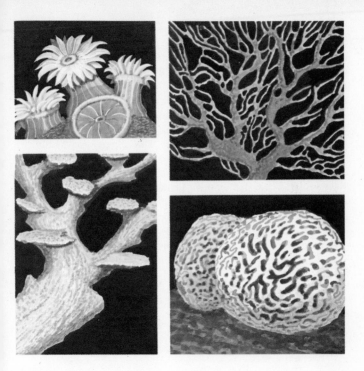

(*Top left*) Magnified coral polyp. (*Top right*) *Gorgonia* red fan coral. (*Bottom left*) Stagshead coral. (*Bottom right*) Brain coral

form the coral reef itself. Inside each tiny polyp are microscopic plant cells which aid the metabolism of the coral polyp. As these plant cells need light, polyps must live in the top layers of the ocean – live polyps seldom occur deeper than 150 feet – so that only the uppermost part of the reef is composed of live animals.

The upper level of growth of the live polyps is controlled by the lowest level of water at neap tides. Polyps are very sensitive to the presence of fresh water. Immediately after the great cyclone which struck eastern Queensland in 1918, parts of the Barrier Reef were flooded with fresh water which came from the land and was carried above the sea water. This resulted in the death of the polyps over the flooded areas.

Many marine animals inhabit the pockets and crevices of the Great Barrier Reef. Among the largest are the giant clams. All six of these species of mollusc are found on the Reef and the largest can be over four and a half feet long. They have been called 'man-eaters' because divers have been caught by the two valves (shells) closing, but this is really a misnomer because these clams actually feed on minute particles of matter which they filter out of the water and an algae which grows within their flesh tissue. The clams are found in lagoons and reef flats, the smaller species being attached to the reef by a stout stalk to prevent their being washed away by the action of the waves. The larger species do not have this stalk as they are heavy enough to stay in place. The lips of the valves are covered by an extension of the body tissues which is called the mantle. This is often very beautifully coloured, and it contains light-sensitive cells which can cause the valves to close when a shadow passes over the clam.

Giant earthworms, thicker than a man's thumb, have been found up to 11 feet long. Here one is compared with a normal-size earthworm. (*Bottom*) A 'squirter' earthworm

The giant clams range up to 4½ feet in length.

GIANT AND 'SQUIRTER' EARTHWORMS

Australia has quite a number of 'largest size' records among animals, and one of the oddest of these is held by the very long earthworms which are found in small well-defined areas in certain parts of the three eastern States. One species, *Megascolides australis* of Victoria, has been found to measure up to eleven feet long when unstretched. The giant species have a peculiar and somewhat aromatic smell; this is probably connected in some way with their digestive processes.

Another earthworm, which can be found under rotting logs in the coastal forest of New South Wales, can defend itself when roughly handled by squirting jets of internal fluids for distances of up to eighteen inches out of small pores which surround the body. These 'squirter' earthworms (*Didymogaster sylvaticus*) are completely harmless, but the squirts effectively startle and discourage any would-be predators.

(*Above*) By 1925, areas such as this were densely infested by prickly pear. (*Below*) The same area after the moth *Cactoblastis cactorum* was introduced.

PRICKLY PEAR AND THE *CACTOBLASTIS* MOTH

Prickly pear is the common name for several species of cactus-like plants whose correct scientific name is *Opuntia*. These plants were originally introduced into Australia as garden decoration, but they soon escaped from the garden environment and spread over a very large area of agricultural land in Queensland and New South Wales. They grew so thickly together that normal methods of control proved useless. By 1925 prickly pears covered some thirty million acres of good farming land and about the same area was threatened with further spread.

As the result of extensive research by biologists, a small moth with the imposing name of *Cactoblastis cactorum* was deliberately liberated in large numbers in the areas of prickly pear. This species was known to feed on prickly pear in America. The moths did very well and spread rapidy, completely destroying the prickly pear over enormous areas. By 1934 the area of land covered by prickly pear in Queensland was estimated to be less than one-tenth of that which had been under the plant ten years before. This is an excellent example of successful biological control of a pest plant species. At the present time the moth is still keeping the prickly pear under control because, as so little prickly pear remains, the present distribution of the food for the moth is in widely scattered but small isolated patches. In some of these areas, *Cactoblastis* is still to be found but the moths are doomed to die out as they eat out the pear. In other patches, the pear is tending to spread but sooner or later each patch is found by the moth which then eats it out. Thus the pear and the moth have reached a sort of equilibrium.

The grub of the *Cactoblastis* moth thrives upon, and only upon, the prickly pear.

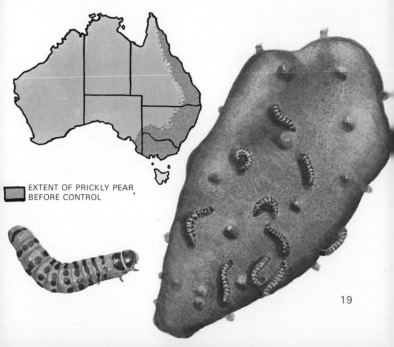

EXTENT OF PRICKLY PEAR
BEFORE CONTROL

19

SPIDERS

Most spiders spin the well-known circular web by which they catch the small insects they eat. The St Andrews Cross spider (*Argyope aetheria*) adds an extra touch by decorating her web with two broad crossed bands of web material which are made by the female discharging whole groups of threads from her many spinnerets. The extra bands draw attention to the web but are thought to deter birds with intention of eating the spider because, as she sits in the centre of her web, the bands look like four very large feet.

The Fisherman Spider (*Dicrostichus furcatus*) catches its food by an apparently unique method among animals. It sits on a bridge of thread, makes a 'line' of fine thread and 'baits' it with a very sticky globule. The spider 'fishes' at night by swinging its two-inch line from one of its front legs. This movement attracts night-flying moths which get caught on the globule and are hauled in by the successful angler.

(*Left*) St Andrews Cross Spider
(*Below*) Fisherman Spider

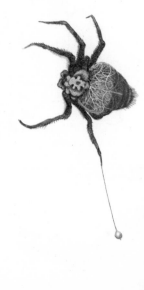

The Red-back Spider (*Latrodectus hasseltii*) is one of the most disliked and dreaded animals in Australia. It lives all over the continent in nooks, crannies and dark places such as are found in old buildings or disused cupboards. Its red back is very obvious and acts as a distinguishing mark to humans and other animals alike. Its normal food consists of insects (especially the larger ground-dwelling beetles), centipedes and wood lice. The bite of the Red-back Spider can cause tremendous pain and even death.

Most small animals which are potentially dangerous to man are usually more than anxious to get away from him when they are disturbed, and so trouble is avoided in many cases. However, the Funnel-web Spider (*Atrax robustus*) is exceedingly dangerous because if it is hungry it will actively attack any moving object, no matter how large. Its main weapons are its very sharp fangs which have highly polished and curved needles on which open five tiny ducts leading

(*Top*) Red-back Spider
(*Bottom*) Funnel-web spider

21

back to the poison sacs. Normally kept folded in grooves beneath the head, the fangs are sunk into any object the Funnel-web wishes to attack. The poison is very strong and is fatal to man, so it is perhaps fortunate that this spider does not occur all over Australia but only in the east coast region. The web is made on the ground to catch small ground dwelling insects which the Funnel-web detects by their movements.

The trap-door spiders

These are an interesting cosmopolitan group of spiders which make and live in holes in the ground. They close off these holes against the weather and predators by a special trap-door.

The trap-door spiders that live in the dense gum-tree forest make fragile trap-doors of the very deep leaf litter which covers the floor of the forest. Insect food here is very plentiful so that the spiders catch their prey within a few inches of their burrows. They have relatively poor eyesight and stoutish short limbs which are useful for moving through the leaf litter but not much good for fast running.

With trap-door spiders that live on the slopes of small creeks the burrow door becomes more of a flap which prevents rain or flowing water from entering the hole. On the

The Brown Trap-door Spider (*Arbanitis fuscipes*) constructs a tunnel in clay soil and closes the entrance with a silk screen.

male

female

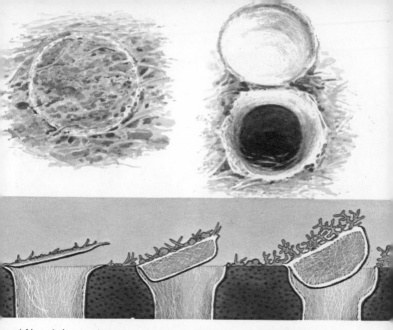

(*Above*) A trap-door closed and open, showing the silk lining
(*Below*) The three basic types of trap-door — the thin, wafer type; a
more substantial type with a bevelled edge; and the 'cork' type, which
is thick and heavily camouflaged and prevents the burrow being
flooded in heavy rainstorms.

other handsome species which live in the bare clay pans of
open woodland must cope with actual flooding so they make
very thick and perfectly fitting doors which act as a cork to
plug the mouth of the burrow completely.

It is in the dry mulga scrub of the more interior areas of
Western Australia that the most interesting adaptations are
met with. Here the ground is covered with long, very thin
twigs and similarly shaped leaves, but there is much less food
about for the spiders. The species living here have much
better eyesight than their woodland cousins and longer,
more athletic legs. They actively hunt for their food over
larger areas of ground. Some species build only light trap-
doors and attach thin twigs to the edge of the burrow which
run out radially from the burrow. The spiders sit in the
burrow and detect their prey as it moves over these twigs.

The aborigines regard 'honey pot' ants as a great delicacy.

INSECTS

Australia has an enormous number of insect species, ranging from troublesome sand flies and midges to very beautiful butterflies and moths. There are a fantastic number of often brightly ornamented beetles, and countless flies, dragon-flies, bugs and bees. Some have little effect on man, others cause great damage to his crops and gardens while still others (see page 18) have been specially imported to control other pests. A few of the interesting ones are described below.

The honey ants (*Camponotus* species) collect the nectar of flowers and honey-like fluids from other insects, and store the honey in a very unusual way. Certain members of the species can enlarge that part of the digestive tract called the crop to a very considerable size. These individuals are fed, indeed literally gorged, by the other ants until they become living honey pots with abdomens so distended that they are quite translucent to light. The 'honey pots' live permanently in the nest and move only a little. The aborigines have a very

A bulldog ant

sweet tooth and yet get few sweet things in their natural diet; they take great pains to search for and dig out the nests of these ants which they eat with gusto.

Another insect regularly eaten by the aborigines is the 'witchetty grub', the larva of a genus of wood moth (*Xyleutes*). This thick large grub lives in the roots of certain shrubs or near the butt of small trees. The aborigines dig out these roots and extract the grub with a specially carved wooden hook. They are eaten alive or cooked and taste like almonds or like scrambled eggs sprinkled with sugar. In some areas witchetty grubs are very important in the diet of the aborigines as they are high in protein.

Bulldog or soldier ants (*Myrmecia* species) are among the largest ants in the world; these monsters can grow to more than an inch long. Although they have only thin spindly bodies, some can jump at least ten times their own length. The guards of the nests of this species have very large mandibles (pincers) in the front of the head. Their sting is extremely painful.

Termites are often called 'white ants' in Australia. This is a misnomer as termites are actually members of a completely different order of insects, the Isoptera. This group has developed very complex systems of social organization. Different members of the colony do specialist jobs of work for the colony as a whole, such as bringing in food, building new galleries inside the mounds in which they live, tending the juvenile stages, defending the mound against intruders, and so on. In many species, the groups which do the different jobs look different from one another as their bodies are modified for the job concerned. This is called the development of *castes*.

Termite mounds are very variable in shape and range from small lumps of clay found at the base of trees to the enormous termitaries of northern Australia which can be over ten feet high and contain millions of termites. The mounds are constructed of chewed-up vegetable matter and earth. This the termites paste in layers which dry to an exceedingly hard substance. In a few species the large mounds are slab-shaped with the broad sides oriented to the sun's rays. As a result

A termite mound in northern Australia, and various termite castes.

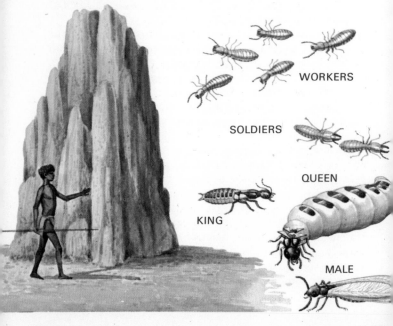

WORKERS

SOLDIERS

QUEEN

KING

MALE

A witchetty grub

the mounds points north and south – a permanent compass for the traveller. Inside the mounds the temperature and the amount of water in the air are closely controlled within very narrow limits. Termites die quickly if exposed to humidities or temperatures outside this range. Therefore they can only leave the mounds when conditions outside are the same as those inside. On these rare occasions winged males and females can be seen flying in fantastic numbers and it is then that mating and the foundation of new mounds and colonies takes place.

Termites eat most vegetable matter and all sorts of dead wood, and are an important link in the ecological food chain. Inside their digestive tracts are special bacteria which can break down the hard outer layer of cellulose which forms the cells of plants. From each termite mound can be found a spreading net of tiny tunnels or galleries in the soil which lead to the food source. Termites can cause considerable financial loss because of their ability to destroy wooden buildings and other human structures such as railway sleepers and telegraph poles.

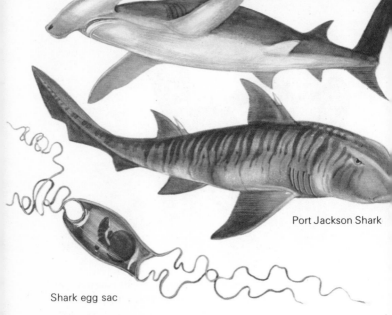

A hammerhead shark

Port Jackson Shark

Shark egg sac

FISHES

Sharks

Fishes are divided into two main groups, the bony fishes and those with cartilaginous skeletons. Sharks belong to the latter, the more primitive of the two groups, having not developed true bone but using cartilage as the frame of the body. Also, instead of true scales they have rough denticles in the skin, some of which are modified to form the many rows of teeth which give the mouth of sharks such a horrifying appearance. As a result of adopting different sorts of food, sharks have developed different types of teeth of specialized shape. Some species are harmless plankton-eaters while others are ferocious flesh-eaters.

About a hundred different species of shark are known from the waters around Australia. A sign of some of them are the 'mermaid's purses' which often get washed ashore on the beach. These are empty egg sacs which formerly contained one or two eggs. These sacs complete with eggs are laid by the female of certain species and attach themselves to seaweed and the like by the small tendrils on their sides. When the young are hatched they escape from the sac by swimming through a slit in its top. In other species of shark, from two to fifty young are nourished inside the female and are born alive and relatively well developed.

Sharks have a justifiably bad reputation for attacking swimmers in the surf of the delightful Australian beaches, and many measures are taken to prevent these often fatal attacks. On some beaches large shark-proof pens have been erected, but more commonly the tower of the life-saving club acts as a look-out point for sighting sharks and also distressed swimmers. The look-outs are often assisted in busy seasons and on popular beaches by small spotter planes which radio the location of sharks sighted to those on shore. There have been many attempts to devise shark repellents to be released into the water when sharks are about. As there is much evidence that sharks have poor eyesight but an excellent sense of underwater chemical detection or 'smell', the substances used, such as copper acetate, are supposed to confuse this sense and act as a sort of 'scent-screen' but they seldom work in practice.

Queensland Lungfish

The Queensland Lungfish

This fascinating animal is a survivor of a very primitive family of fish, the Ceratodidae, which dates back thirty-five million years to the Triassic Period. Only six species survive to the present day, the others being found in South America and in Africa. The Australian species, called the Queensland Lungfish (*Neoceratodus forsteri*), was found in two rivers in central Queensland, the Burnett and Mary Rivers (see map) and has been successfully introduced into neighbouring rivers. These rivers, like many others in the centre of the continent, flow only for restricted periods of the year so that the fish must cope with a habitat where the pools are often drying up or decreasing in size. To do this, the Queensland Lungfish has its swim bladder modified into an un-fish-like respiratory organ which opens into the front end of the digestive tract. This organ acts as a primitive sort of lung so that the animal can survive for longish periods out of the water. Actually the Australian lungfish is less dependent on this organ as a source of oxygen than its two cousins, as under certain circumstances they can derive up to ninety-five per cent of their oxygen from air gulped into their swim bladders from above the water surface. The African species form mud cocoons around themselves when the rivers dry up. Individuals have been known to survive as long as four years in this way.

The Queensland Lungfish grows up to six feet long and lays its eggs on the muddy bottom of pools. It can easily be recognized from all other fish by a very primitive feature, the presence of lobes on its fins. In recently evolved fishes the fin is supported entirely by rays which emerge from the

30

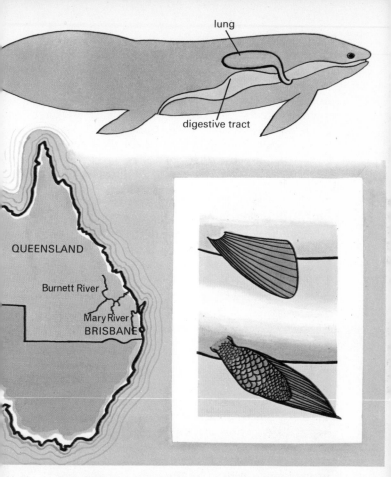

Unlike the fins of other fish (*above*), the fins of lungfish (*below*) arise from a limb-like lobe.

surface of the body proper, but in lungfish these rays arise from a lobe which is rather limb-like as it contains some skeletal bones. This 'limb' helps the lungfish in moving across mud. The species eats water weeds and small crustaceans and molluscs, such as bottom-living snails, and has specially modified grinding teeth plates on the lower jaw to cope with this sort of diet.

The Queensland Groper

The Queensland Groper (*Promicrops lanceolatus*) is one of the largest members of the group of bony fishes. It is found in bays and estuaries of the coasts of Queensland and Western Australia. This giant has been recorded up to 800 pounds in weight and over six feet long; weights of 200 and 300 pounds are not uncommon. The Queensland Groper lives on the bottom and tends to hide its great bulk in rocky or coral caves. It is much feared by skin divers whom it will stalk and even attack when they pass its well camouflaged resting place.

The Mudskipper

A common feature of the northern coasts of Australia is the extensive mangrove swamps, where considerable areas of mud are exposed at low tide. These mud flats have a varied and interesting fauna, one of the most fascinating species being the little Mudskipper (*Periophthalmus australis*). This

Queensland Groper

Mudskipper

fish has very muscular forefins and moves around on the surface of the mud with a very comical hopping action, using its tail and fins. It can even climb the roots of the mangrove trees and can be seen eyeing the world from this vantage point with its very large and protruding eyes.

When the tide is out, the Mudskippers can be seen basking in the sun a few inches from the holes into which they retreat should danger arise. Each animal defends its hole with great vigour and they can often be seen fighting over the owner-ship of a particular hole in the mud. As well as the usual gills behind the head, Mudskippers have a specially modified part of the tail which acts as a type of auxiliary gill and is usually kept beneath the surface of the water in a shallow mud pool. The Mudskipper is so well adapted to living out of water that there have even been reports saying they will drown if kept submerged for long periods of time.

AMPHIBIANS AND REPTILES

The frogs of Australia

Australia has a varied frog fauna, many members of which are especially adapted to living in habitats where rainfall is often very slight and irregular. Their behaviour is such that only under precise and correct conditions of wetness and temperature will the males start calling to attract the females to the often temporary waters where mating takes place. By the time the ponds have dried up, the young of these species will have very quickly developed from eggs, through tadpoles, to fully grown adults, so that in this form they can survive the drier periods until the next wet season. Other special sorts of adaptations to the sometimes peculiar Australian environment have occurred and two examples are given here.

The very strange-looking Turtle Frog (*Myobatrachus gouldii*) is only found in the south-west corner of Western Australia. Its special turtle-like body shape has developed to help it move through the sandy soils in which it lives. It moves through the soil by digging with its short powerful

Turtle Frog

front legs and pushing the sand behind its body with its back legs. Its major diet is termites and it is often found inside their mounds or under logs where they are living. It slowly moves through the termites' galleries and feeds until its stomach is filled to capacity.

Living perpetually underground presents a problem for a type of animal whose young normally develop in free water. However, the termite-eating frog has exceedingly large and yolky eggs which suggests that the tadpole stage of development takes place in either a pool of jelly formed by a group of eggs or in the egg itself.

The Water-holding Frog (*Cyclorana platycephalus*) lives in central Australia. When the stream or pond in which it lives begins to dry up, it digs down deeply into the mud or into the bank with its body absolutely swollen full of water. There it makes a little cell while the mud dries up around it. When enough rain falls to fill the stream or pond above, the mud around the frog gets wet and it burrows to the surface to carry on with its life cycle. The aborigines have learned of its habits and use it as a source of water when drought is on the land.

The Water-holding Frog

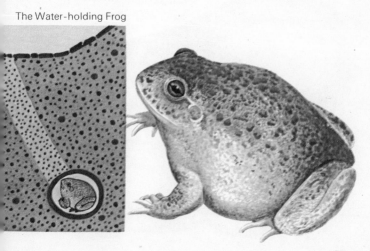

Sea snakes

The reptiles are a group of animals which used to occur in far greater numbers on the earth in previous geological ages. In those times they occupied many different habitats, flying in the air and swimming in the water as well as living on land. The sea snakes (family Hydrophiidae) are a much more recent group which have taken to the sea after evolving originally on land. They breathe air but have special flaps or valves over their nostrils to prevent the entry of water when they submerge. Unlike the terrestrial snakes which have a small opening on the tip of the upper jaw, the sea snakes can completely close off their mouth openings. Other marine adaptations are a broad flattened tail and a mode of swimming by vertical undulations unlike the horizontal wrigglings of their earth-bound cousins.

A number of species of sea snake are found in the waters around Australia. They prefer warmer water and are thus generally found in northern seas. Sea snakes feed on fish and

Yellow-bellied
Sea Snake

Black-banded Sea Snake

sometimes eels and have an extremely powerful venom which probably developed to kill active and fast-moving prey such as fish. Their means of breeding is something of a mystery although they are known to produce live young. There have been reports of great aggregations of sea snakes, the most amazing being a mass of intertwined sea snakes about ten yards wide and over sixty miles long which was seen by a ship travelling between Sumatra and the Malay archipelago. Sea snakes can grow to over six feet long and are often plagued by marine growths, such as barnacles, on their bodies.

The Yellow-bellied Sea Snake (*Pelamis platurus*) and the Black-banded Sea Snake (*Laticauda laticaudata*) both grow to about three feet. They are widespread in the Indian Ocean and the western Pacific, occurring as far south as Sydney in the case of the former and Tasmania in the case of the latter.

Blind Snake

North Queensland Python

Snakes of Australia

Australia has many species of snakes but the main group consists of species which have their fangs emerging from the front of the upper and lower jaws. This feature is in contrast to species common in other parts of the world which have their fangs hinged at the rear of their jaws. As well as these two groups, other sorts of snake include the so-called blind snakes and members of the python and boa families, all of which are represented in the Australian herpetological fauna.

The Blind Snake (*Typhlops bituberculatus*) is a pretty animal. It has a head which merges into the body in such a way that it is sometimes hard to tell which end is which. It has a very shiny appearance and only extremely rudimentary eyes. The body is very supple and when it is captured the snake tends to 'swim' through the fingers of the hand. This

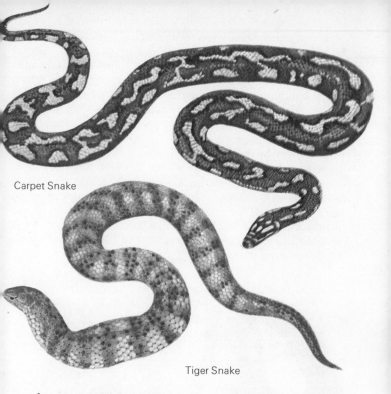

Carpet Snake

Tiger Snake

suppleness means that the animal can literally tie itself in
knots. Blind Snakes are found in the upper layers of loose soil
or under decaying logs and they feed on ants, termites and
other small insects.

The North Queensland Python (*Python amethystinus*) is the
largest Australian snake. This species has been reliably
measured at over twenty feet long and holds fourth place in
the world's length records for snakes. Like many of the
larger snakes this species can undergo extremely long fasts in
captivity and probably in the wild. It kills its prey by crushing and asphyxiating it in its body coils, and its normal diet
consists of smaller mammals and even birds. It has been
known occasionally to tackle larger meals and the picture is
based on an authentic record of a specimen having swallowed
a wallaby.

The Carpet Snake (*Morelia spilotes variegata*) is very common over the northern areas of Australia. This snake is often kept as a household pet because it does not attack man but is very fond of small vermin such as mice and rats which cause trouble wherever they are found. Unfortunately this rather harmless and attractive snake has a skin which is much prized for handbags or shoes so that it is frequently killed for this purpose.

The Tiger Snake (*Notechis scutatus*), although quite small in size, usually about three and a half feet long, is one of Australia's most venomous snakes. It is found usually in swampy areas or along river banks and is a good swimmer. A very dangerous species, it is responsible for most of the deaths from snake-bite in Australia. It normally feeds on frogs and the many species of lizards. Up to fifty young can be produced each year by a single female.

Copperhead

Common Brown Snake

(TAIPAN IS SIMILAR IN APPEARANCE.)

Australian Coral Snake

Bandy Bandy

The Common Brown Snake (*Demansia textilis*) lives in open or lightly wooded country and has very variable colour patterns, ranging from light to dark brown, often with black bands across the body. It is a very fast-moving animal, aggressive and very venomous, though less so than the Tiger Snake.

The Copperhead (*Denisonia superba*) is an attractively marked species. It is a more sluggish animal of often considerable length (up to six feet). It lives generally in hilly country but can often be found in swampy areas. Its normal diet consists of frogs and small native mice.

The Australian Coral Snake (*Rhynchoelaps australis*) and the Bandy Bandy (*Furina annulata*) are both completely harmless to man but are still needlessly persecuted. They are particularly attractively coloured but very little is known about their way of life.

The Tuatara

The term 'living fossil' has been applied to many different animals of which both New Zealand and Australia have more than their fair share. One of the best examples of a living fossil is the Tuatara (*Sphenodon punctatus*) of New Zealand, which is the last surviving species of a whole group of reptiles called the Rhynchocephalia. Many species of this type of reptile once roamed the earth but with the exception of the Tuatara they all became extinct at least a hundred million years ago. A feature of the group was the presence of a curved and rather beak-like notch in the upper jaw and the presence of two cavities in the side of the skull, a feature found in no other living reptile. Another primitive feature is the presence of 'floating' abdominal ribs in the body as well as the usual 'true' ribs which are attached to the backbone. Like some lizards, the Tuatara has a vestigial third eye on top of the head, with a corresponding opening in the skull. However, this 'pineal eye' conveys no sensation of light to the brain.

Today the Tuatara is confined to the islands of Cook Strait and a few islands off the north coast of the North Island. It is completely protected by law and the number of visitors to these islands is very closely controlled so that the Tuatara has the maximal chance of survival. The animals live in burrows which they either excavate themselves or appro-

Tuatara

priate from the many burrowing sea birds on these islands. Their diet consists mainly of beetles, and especially favoured is a large wingless cricket called *weta* by the Maoris. Occasionally the Tuatara will eat the eggs of the sea birds.

Breeding takes place in early summer, the female laying from ten to fifteen eggs in a parchment-like membrane. The eggs are buried in the sand and left unattended until they hatch some fifteen months later. The young break through the egg with a caruncle (a conical projection on the tip of the snout) – a special feature which is only found in two other groups of reptiles, the crocodiles and the turtles. Breeding first takes place when the Tuataras are from twenty to thirty years old, but this is a very long-lived species which is considered to live in excess of fifty years. This makes it probably the slowest growing of all land animals.

One of the Tuatara's favourite foods is the *weta*.

Goannas

The largest living lizards in the world belong to the family Varanidae, the monitors or dragons. Eighteen of the twenty-five living species of the group are found in Australia, and they are all characterized by having strong limbs and claws and a very powerful tail which is usually flattened laterally. Unlike other lizards, goannas cannot regrow their tail if it is broken. The word 'goanna' is thought to be a corruption of 'iguana', a common name used for similar reptiles in other parts of the world, but it may be derived from an aboriginal word.

All the goannas have a very liberal taste and can eat almost any type of foodstuff which becomes available to them, including smaller lizards and insects. They are especially fond of carrion, so that their bite is often dangerous as the wound can become infected. Australian goannas can be divided into three main groups. The arboreal or tree-climbing goannas retreat to trees which they climb rapidly when disturbed. Unfortunately they have poor eyesight so that if a human figure is the closest upright object they will climb up that and they can cause severe lacerations with their sharp claws. The ground-dwelling goannas live in burrows and are very fast runners. They often rise off their forelegs when moving at

Perentie

Gould's Monitor

Lace Monitor

speed and run for long distances on their hind limbs only, using their tail as a balance. They are usually associated with rocky outcrops or stony places. The semi-aquatic goannas have special flaps to close their nostrils while swimming, and use their broad flat tail as a vertical paddle. Unlike their ground-living relations, their nostrils are situated at the top of the snout to reduce the amount of head showing above water.

The largest living lizard species is the Komodo Dragon (*Varanus komodoensis*), which can be over twelve feet long and is found on several islands in Indonesia. The second largest is the central Australian Perentie or Perentjie (*Varanus giganteus*), which can exceed eight feet in length. This species fights by grasping its opponent's front legs and trying to unbalance him by swinging its heavy tail.

Scaly-foot

Pretty Snake Lizard

Sharp-snouted Snake
Lizard

Snake lizards

The Pygopodidae are a group of lizards which have altered
their body form so much as to look like snakes. However,
they can easily be recognized from snakes by two simple
characters. Firstly they have a small oval ear opening located
just behind the eye, whereas true snakes have no ear opening
at all. Secondly their tails are longer than their head and body
length whereas snakes have tails which make up less than a
fifth of their total body length. Practically all the species in
this family are found in Australia or Papua.

The Scaly-foot (*Pygopus lepidopodus*) has small flaps at the
rear of its body which are vestigial legs. Up to two feet long,
it lives in peaty earth where it makes a tunnel of about a
finger's diameter and forty inches long. It normally feeds on
small insects.

The Pretty Snake Lizard (*Aprasia pulchella*) frequents
loose sandy soil. It is about two feet long when full grown.

The Sharp-snouted Snake Lizard or Burton's Legless
Lizard (*Lialis burtonii*) is a dweller of grasslands and the
leaf-mould of the woodland floor. Like many other reptiles,
it has the ability to voluntarily break off its tail when pur-
sued. This distracts would-be predators and enables the
animal to escape.

Bobtail, with newborn offspring half the size of the parent

The Bobtail (*Trachydosaurus rugosus*) is probably the best known reptile in Australia, as can be judged from its many common names – Stumpy-tail, Pine-cone Lizard, Shingle-back, to mention a few. It is a very common, sluggish animal, and is found in patches of bush in and around the suburbs of some Australian cities, so that it will have been seen at close quarters by most Australians. The Bobtail's only defence is surprise, and when it is disturbed it will suddenly open its bright pink mouth, stick out its blue tongue and emit a loud hiss – all of which adds up to a quite startling but harmless effect. This animal can bite with considerable strength and it holds on very tightly once attached, but its teeth are tiny and can do little damage. Because of its slow mobility and habit of warming itself on the warm bitumen of suburban roads, the Bobtail is a frequent victim of the motor car and many are killed this way.

The Bobtail does not lay eggs like most reptiles but produces live young. Only one or two are born and they are extremely large, being from one third to one half the size of the mother. A vegetarian, the Bobtail feeds mainly on berries and fruits of ground-spreading plants but will also eat small lizards, when they can be caught, and snails and slugs.

Agamas or dragon lizards

The Military Dragon (*Amphibolurus maculatus*) acquired its common name in the days when soldiers wore bright red uniforms, as it has bright reddish colours on the side of its body. It lives in sandy and sparsely timbered country and can often be seen running with great speed from grass tussock to grass tussock. Other members of the Agama group frequent open rock faces where they can be seen sunning themselves in the warm sun or can be found huddled together under slabs of exfoliated rock during cooler weather. Some species are territorial and divide the rock face into definite areas which they defend against intruders of the same sex.

The Painted Dragon (*Amphibolurus pictus*) is a particularly brightly coloured species which alters its colours at different times of the year. This characteristic is probably related to the breeding condition of the individual animal.

When threatened with attack, the Bearded Dragon (*Amphibolurus barbatus*) opens its mouth and thus erects a great circlet of spines under its chin. This startling display acts as a

Military Dragon

Bearded Dragon

Painted Dragon

discouragement to any animal with designs on the Bearded Dragon as a meal.

A much larger tropical species, the Frilled Lizard (*Chlamydosaurus kingii*) is found in northerly areas. Like the Bearded Dragon, its main defence is to erect its very large frill, open its mouth and hiss. A much faster moving species, it will often rise up on its back legs and run bipedally.

The Mountain or Thorny Devil (*Moloch horridus*) is one of the most astonishing-looking of all Australian animals. This little creature looks very fearsome but is completely harmless and certainly does not deserve its specific name. It lives almost entirely on ants and will sit beside an ant trail methodically picking off every passing ant with its sticky tongue. Living often in dry areas, it has an amazing system for collecting the dew which falls on its back. The fluid moves through the blotting-paper-like outer skin layer and travels to water-absorbent pads at the corner of the Mountain Devil's mouth. It is there expressed into the mouth cavity by a chewing action.

Mountain Devil

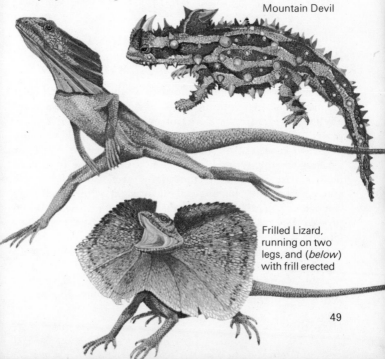

Frilled Lizard, running on two legs, and (*below*) with frill erected

49

Emu with chicks

BIRDS
The Emu

The Emu (*Dromaius novaehollandiae*) is the bird which most people associate with Australia. Australians themselves obviously regard it as a sort of avian symbol as it has repeatedly figured on stamps, coins and so on. Emus have many primitive features. As well as their inability to fly, their feathers are highly modified and two shafts arise from each feather base. Because of their large size, Emus have few enemies, and they have excellent eyesight with which they can detect potential trouble a very long distance away. When pressed they can run at high speeds and they have been timed moving at more than thirty miles per hour.

Emus form pairs in the middle of summer and remain together for five months. In early winter the hen lays five to twenty large greenish eggs, each weighing one and a half to two pounds. They are laid in a shallow nest which is placed on the ground in such a way that the sitting bird can see for a distance all around. Once the eggs are laid, the hen loses all interest in their maintenance and the incubation is carried out by the cock. He sits on the eggs constantly for eight weeks, using up layers of fat stored in his body. Once hatched the chicks follow their father for perhaps a year. At first they are quite brightly striped, but at about six months their body coloration changes to the dull parental pattern.

The main food of Emus consists of seeds of different types. They will also eat grass, leaves, fruit and flowers. The seeds of various species of mulga (*Acacia*) scrub are important and in winter the green seed pods of *Cassia* are especially favoured. When insects are plentiful, they act as a source of protein for the Emus. If the rains fail and the food supply gets low in any particular area, Emus migrate in large numbers to areas where food is more plentiful. In modern times this has meant their arrival in farming areas where they do great damage to the crops. Because of these movements, Emu-proof fences have been erected in Western Australia to impede their migrations, and at times great numbers of Emus can be seen along these fences.

(*Above*) Emu fence. (*Below left*) Emu egg with chicken egg for comparison. (*Below right*) Emu nest

The Cassowary

The Australian Cassowary (*Casuarius casuarius*) is Australia's second large and flightless bird. Cassowaries are more common in New Guinea and Papua although the Australian Cassowary is also found in tropical Queensland. A stocky thick-set bird, it is an inhabitant of jungle and dense tropical scrub. There are actually three species of cassowary and they each stand between three and five feet high. They live on fallen flowers and fruits on the jungle floor. Insects are also eaten when available.

Little is known about the biology of the cassowaries as they are difficult to see among the dense vegetation. They have a shield-like helmet on the top of the head which is apparently used when they force their way through the jungle creepers and branches. Cassowaries lay three to five greenish eggs in a nest made directly on the jungle floor. They fight among themselves at certain seasons using a greatly lengthened claw on the inside of each foot.

Australian Cassowary

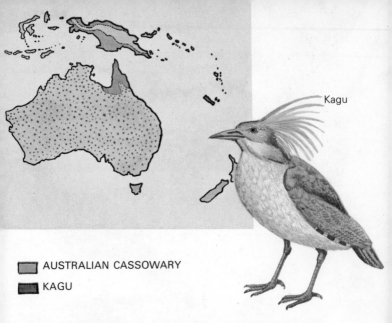

AUSTRALIAN CASSOWARY

KAGU

The Kagu of New Caledonia

The Kagu (*Rhynochetos jubatus*) is the only species in a family of birds called the Rhynochetidae. It is a rather strange-looking bird which is found only on the island of New Caledonia. A frequenter of mountainous regions, the Kagu lives in dense vegetation and is hardly able to fly at all. It progresses by long hops from bush to bush and is active mainly at night. The Kagu is a very noisy bird, making a loud screaming, yelping cry which can be heard over long distances. The nest of twigs and leaves is made on the ground and only a single egg is laid. The courting dance is a rather crazy display of leaping and running about in a disjointed sort of manner. The male Kagu uses small objects such as sticks and stones in his display dance. As a warning to other animals, the Kagu opens its wings in a wide lateral display in a very similar manner to the Sun Bittern of South America, which is probably a close relative. The Kagu itself is considered to be an aberrant relative of the cranes and rails. Unfortunately this unique and weird bird is in danger of extinction because of human development.

53

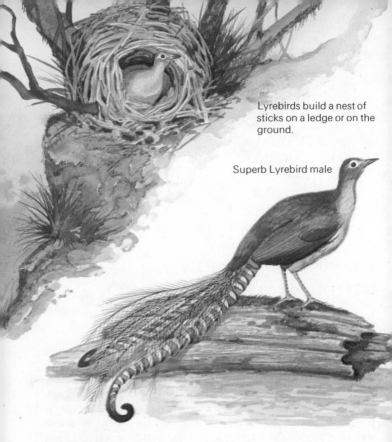

Lyrebirds build a nest of sticks on a ledge or on the ground.

Superb Lyrebird male

Lyrebirds

Many bird lovers and bushmen have been completely fooled by the amazing mimicry of the two species of lyrebird, the Superb Lyrebird (*Menura novaehollandiae*) and Albert's Lyrebird (*Menura alberti*). Not only can they imitate with astonishing accuracy the calls of all other birds they hear, but they can reproduce perfectly the various sounds that men make in the bush, such as the noise of chopping wood and the buzz of wood saws. On occasion they have been heard imitating barking dogs and even the noise of a railway train. The male is the better mimic but the female also has a respectable repertoire of imitative sounds.

Lyrebirds belong to a family of birds which has no members outside Australia. They pair for life and the male performs a very elaborate and stately courtship dance before mating. The male sings loudly from a small cleared area in the bush, and as the song becomes more intense the long and delicate tail slowly rises upwards and then forwards until it is over the head of the displaying bird. The beautiful spreading tail completely covers the head and body and is apparently very attractive to the female as the male dances and struts to and fro. Only a single egg is laid each year which means that the lyrebird has a very slow rate of recruitment. This type of animal is always in particular danger when some external factors affect its way of life. Lyrebirds are now completely protected, but were once slaughtered in great numbers for the feathers in their lovely tails.

After the egg is laid, the female incubates it in a large nest of sticks which is built on the ground or more often on a projecting rocky ledge. The male has very little to do with the raising of the young. Lyrebirds live in dense thickets of forest in mountainous areas, and because of their size in this habitat of thick vegetation, can fly for only short distances.

Superb Lyrebird male displaying

The Mutton-bird

The correct name for this large sea-going bird is the Short-tailed Shearwater (*Puffinus tenuirostris*). The name 'Mutton-bird' is also used in New Zealand to describe the Sooty Shearwater (*Puffinus griseus*). A source of food since colonial times, these and other species of petrel are still exploited for their flesh, especially on the islands of Bass Strait between Tasmania and the Australian mainland.

The species has a very interesting life history which is now well known as the result of years of research into its general biology. The Mutton-birds arrive at the breeding grounds during the last week in September and there they dig burrows in the sand or re-excavate old ones. This work is only done at night, the birds arriving at the burrow at sunset. Because a number of the birds have been marked by ringing and then recaptured over several years, it is known that many of the Mutton-birds return to exactly the same burrow year after year. After the burrows are prepared, the birds leave the islands and do not return for about three weeks.

The migration route of the Mutton-bird (Short-tailed Shearwater)

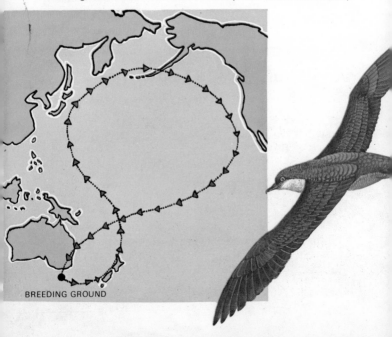

BREEDING GROUND

Mutton-birds nest in burrows in the sand.

However, whatever the weather and external food conditions, the birds return, and egg laying on the Bass Strait islands always takes place between November 20 and December 2. A single large egg, about one seventh of the female's own weight, is laid, and both parents take turns to incubate it for about fifty-five days. The male takes the first shift of up to two weeks and fasts during that period. Although shear-waters are graceful flyers, they are very poor pilots when it comes to landing, having never progressed beyond the crash-landing technique. This is very dangerous, as can be judged from the number of corpses of crashed birds which are seen on the colony. Once the chick is born it is fed on a mixture of regurgitated fish and a special nutritious stomach oil.

Once breeding is completed, the Short-tailed Shearwaters set out on a remarkable migration route (see map) which leads them high into the northern Pacific in a figure-of-eight. This pattern has been determined by the recovery of ringed birds from various places along the migration route. For most of the journey the birds fly roughly in the direction of the prevailing wind, so that their long voyage is something of an 'assisted passage'.

57

Sulphur-crested
Cockatoo

Galah

Great Black Cockatoo

Parrots and cockatoos

Australia and New Zealand have many species of birds be-
longing to the family Psittacidae – the parrots and cockatoos
– those raucous noise-makers of avian society. The illustrations show how colourful are these fascinating birds. The
cockatoos are the larger members of the family and have very
heavy, strong beaks which they use for stripping the bark
from the trunks of trees and thus breaking into the surface of
the wood in search of grubs. Their crests can be erected and

Major Mitchell Cockatoo

Kakapo

are used in display, giving the cockatoos or 'cockies' an extremely comical appearance. The White Cockatoo is a very popular cage bird which occurs in the wild in such large flocks that they may appear like a small white cloud flying by. The name of the grey and pink Galah (*Cacatua rosei-capella*) has been incorporated into Australian slang to describe a prattling or idiotic person but it is not talkative in the wild state.

There is no doubt that Australia's most famous avian export is the pretty little Budgerigar (*Melopsittacus undulatus*). This attractive little bird occurs in very great flocks in the inland, but the overseas bird lover may be astonished to find that all the budgies are basically a grass green colour. The many other colour forms are the result of careful breeding by cage bird fanciers.

New Zealand also has a number of parrots, including two of the strangest species in the family. The Kakapo or Owl Parrot (*Strigops habroptilus*) is a very rare parrot which has lost the power of flight. It runs rapidly through the forest along little paths, but astonishingly enough it feeds on a relatively bird-like diet by climbing up trees for fruit and nectar and then gliding down to the ground. The Kea (*Nestor notabilis*) is a very hardy species which lives in a most unusual environment for parrots, which are mainly a tropical group. The Kea inhabits the highland areas of New Zealand

Kea

The wild Budgerigar (*below*) and various domestic colour varieties

and can be seen to be very active in the snow. During summer it lives on a normal parrot-like diet of fruit, buds and nectar, but in winter the Kea becomes a scavenger and will eat sheep carcasses as carrion. There have even been reports of Keas climbing on to the backs of live sheep and killing them by pecking into their backs to get at the kidney fat.

During the day the Tawny Frogmouth perches motionless (*above*) with its eyes closed and head up, looking like a broken branch

The Tawny Frogmouth

The Tawny Frogmouth (*Podargus strigoides*) is a member of a group of birds that have an exceptionally large and gaping mouth and a triangular hooked bill. They frequent forested savannah and open hardwood forest, and during daylight hours they perch completely motionless on a branch with their head in a rather strange posture. In this way the frogmouths look exactly like a broken branch and are very difficult to distinguish from the tree on which they are perching. Beetles, centipedes, scorpions and crawling insects are their main diet, and some writers have even described insects actively crawling into the open mouth of the bird while it sits motionless in its camouflage posture. Other items of prey are eaten as well, even small mice.

Frogmouths are lethargic during the daytime and in their general body movements, as they have short legs with small and rather weak feet. During the night they make a soft booming call.

The Flock Pigeon

The early explorers and naturalists who visited the central part of Australia described enormous flocks of these pigeons (*Histriophaps histrionica*) which abounded in such great numbers that the sound of their wings as they took flight was described as 'deafening'. By about 1920, however, none of these birds had been seen for many years and bird lovers thought they were extinct. Since then the species has suddenly reappeared in some numbers on several occasions. The numbers seem to have been reduced by the introduction of sheep and cattle; these have reduced the grass seeds which are the main food of the Flock Pigeon (and indeed many other native birds). Fortunately the status of the species means that it is possible to save it from extinction – the fate which overtook the Passenger Pigeon (*Ectopistes migratorius*), a very similar type of bird which once occurred in enormous numbers in the United States, but which has now completely vanished.

Flock Pigeon

Western Magpies confront their neighbours at the boundaries of their territories.

Magpies and butcherbirds

This family, the Cracticidae, only occurs in Australia and New Guinea. They are excellent songsters with some powers of mimicry of other bird calls. An unusual feature is that both sexes can sing either the same song or a different song in response to the call of the other sex. Some species in the group have an interesting territorial system whereby small groups of birds defend their joint home areas. Both sexes may live inside these territories and defend them against intruders in prolonged battles at the frontiers.

Like many Australian and New Zealand birds, the Western Magpie (*Gymnorhina dorsalis*) was originally named by home-sick British settlers with memories of a similar-looking but entirely unrelated species found in Britain. During the nesting season the Western Magpie builds an elaborate bowl-shaped nest which is very neatly lined with wool, leaves, grass or bark. Actually the birds will utilize any sort of material to make and line this nest. Magpies have been known to make nests of wire – even barbed wire – and one nest which was dismantled by a statistically minded bird lover in Western Australia was found to contain $13\frac{3}{4}$ pounds of wire in short pieces whose total length came to 338 feet.

The Grey Butcherbird (*Cracticus torquatus*) is common over most of Australia and Tasmania.

The butcherbirds (*Cracticus* species) are so named because of their somewhat macabre method of storing food. After they have killed the large insects, small birds or mammals that they feed on, these are wedged into small forks or impaled on twigs to help the bird dismember them. Surplus food may be stored. Other food consists of fruit and the occasional small lizard. Territorial behaviour is seen during the breeding season.

Birds of paradise

Of all the many and varied birds known to man, these are surely the most beautiful. The fantastic and varied colours of the males are outstanding among birds and for many years they have attracted attention from bird lovers and others interested in beautiful things. This group of birds is only found in the highlands of New Guinea and Papua and unfortunately many of the 350 known species are thought to be in danger of extinction. This is due to the depredations of skin collectors, and also to the fact that the natives use the multicoloured and sometimes bizarre feathers in their great ceremonial headdresses.

In the early days of the collection and classification of birds, none of the skins which arrived in Europe had feet attached, due to the native method of preparing bird skins. This gave rise to great speculation and it was thought that these birds actually had no feet, so they were given the family name Apodidae (which in Latin means 'no feet'). Biologists of philosophical bent cogitated on this lack of feet and called the birds 'birds of paradise' because their beauty was so much in excess of anything seen before on earth. It was believed by many that the birds spent their whole life in the air, never alighting on the ground, and that nature had not therefore provided them with feet!

Magnificent Riflebird (*Craspedophora magnifica*), northern Australia and New Guinea

(*Left*) Early specimens such as this King of Saxony Bird of Paradise led Europeans to believe that birds of paradise were legless. (*Right*) Red-plumed Bird of Paradise (*Paradisaea apoda raggiana*), New Guinea

Twelve-wired Bird of Paradise (*Seleucides ignotus*), New Guinea

Wilson's Bird of Paradise
(*Diphyllodes respublica*),
New Guinea

Little King Bird of Paradise
(*Cicinnurus regius*), New
Guinea

Superb Bird of Paradise
(*Lophorina superba*), New
Guinea

68

Prince Rudolph's Blue
Bird of Paradise
(*Paradisaea rudolphi*),
New Guinea

Magnificent Bird of
Paradise (*Diphyllodes
magnificus*), New Guinea

Mudnest builders

The family of mudnest builders (Grallinidae) make a deep bowl-shaped nest, usually high up on a horizontal branch. The mud is matted together with grass for strength and is usually lined with fur or feathers.

The name of the Peewit (*Grallina cyanoleuca*) is derived from its call. It is also known as the Magpie-lark. Peewits mate for life and both sexes defend their territory together. The pairs have an unusual system of social communication in that one will start the dual call with 'te-he' and the other will follow immediately with 'pee-o-wit'. The pair will nest in the same locality for several years running and both parents look after the young. In the winter their territorial instinct gives way to gregariousness, and they form small flocks.

The Grey Jumper or Apostle Bird (*Struthidea cinerea*) hops in a characteristic fashion from branch to branch, often making quite long jumps. The name Apostle Bird comes from its habit of associating in small flocks of around twelve birds.

Peewit or Magpie-lark

Apostle Bird or Grey Jumper

The Kookaburra will learn to feed from the hand. It kills snakes by dropping them until they are dead.

The Kookaburra

The popular Kookaburra (*Dacelo gigas*), is also known as the Laughing Jackass or Bushman's Clock. The first of these two popular names refers to the bird's characteristic loud cackling, chuckling call. The second name probably comes from its supposed habit of making the call three times a day.

Kookaburras are easily tamed and many individuals come to suburban back-doors for a free handout. Their normal diet consists of lizards, small rodents and insects, and they also have a fascinating method of killing snakes by either flaying the snake against a projecting branch or repeatedly dropping it from a height until it is dead. Originally only found in the eastern States, the Kookaburra was successfully introduced into Western Australia about 1900.

The brush-tongued honeyeaters

As a part of the process of utilizing food from every available source, many animals have developed and modified special parts of their bodies so that they can obtain food from otherwise inaccessible places. Birds of the family Meliphagidae are good examples of this phenomenon, as they all have specially modified mouth parts to obtain nectar from flowers. Their beak is lengthened and curved for probing into the flowers, and the tongue is also curved on each side and can be pursed up to form a tube which is used to suck up nectar. The somewhat horny tip of the tongue is frayed out into a brush shape which brushes off the pollen at the flower's base.

With two exceptions – an extinct bird from Hawaii with the peculiar name of the O-o, and another species from South Africa – all the members of this family are found in the Australasian region. In many cases the birds have assumed an important role in the fertilization of various flowers and trees as they transfer pollen while they are obtaining nectar. In some cases their bills are so highly modified that the birds

Western Spinebill

concentrate on certain types of flowers of a particular shape only. Our picture shows an example of this in that the Western Spinebill (*Acanthorhynchus superciliosus*) has a bill which is especially suitable for feeding on the long flowers of the kangaroo paw or banksia. As is common among birds, the plumage of many species in this family varies between the sexes. However, in one New Guinea species the system seems to have gone slightly crazy, because although in most areas the sexes have different colours, in other areas both sexes of the same species have the feather colours of the cock and in other areas both sexes have the feather colours of the hen.

An interesting New Zealand species of honeyeater, the Tui (*Prosthemadena novaeseelandiae*) has two tufts of curly white feathers at its throat. These gave rise to its other common name of Parson Bird, because of their resemblance to the neckwear of religious gentlemen of an earlier era. The Tui has a very varied and musical song and is also an excellent mimic.

Tui

The Black Swan

The earliest white men to see Australia were Dutchmen sailing from the Cape of Good Hope to the islands of the Indies and Batavia (now Indonesia and Malaysia). Their course took them eastwards across the Indian Ocean and then northwards, but many of the navigators miscalculated with the poor navigational instruments of the seventeenth and eighteenth centuries, and were thus wrecked on the coast of Western Australia. As a result, the cautious burghers of Holland sent a number of expeditions to investigate these southern shores, and these early explorers commented freely on the strange animals and plants that they saw. To Europeans, whose swans were always a creamy and delicate white, surely one of the strangest reports must have been that of William de Vlamingh who reported numbers of *black* swans seen on a voyage in 1697.

Actually, the Black Swan (*Chenopis atrata*), though a symbol of the State of Western Australia, is found in many places over the southern part of the continent, usually on lakes, swamps or estuaries. The habits of this species are much like its northern paler cousin, especially with regard to its pattern of nest building. It builds its nest on a platform of rushes or reeds in a protected place in shallow water or on a small island. Like white swans, the Black Swan is extremely aggressive to intruders, especially when the young are hatched, and can be a dangerous adversary as it attacks with lunging bill and striking wing.

Black Swan

Brolgas dancing

The Brolga

The Brolga (*Grus rubicundra*) is a very attractive member of the crane family, and is sometimes known as the Native Companion. Standing about 4 feet high, it lives in the north-eastern and some southern parts of Australia and in New Guinea and is extending its range southwards into Western Australia. Unlike other cranes the Brolga lays its eggs on the ground, sometimes without any nest. Its call is a hoarse trumpeting sound. Small groups of Brolgas occasionally perform beautiful and stately dances which are not apparently always associated with mating behaviour but can be a general expression of the excitement of the group. The dance forms the basis of corroborees performed by the aborigines and has even inspired choreographers of modern ballet.

75

Little Penguins coming ashore

The Little Penguin

The smallest penguin in the world is the sixteen-inch long Little Penguin, also called the Blue or Fairy Penguin (*Eudyptula minor*). It is found in Stewart Island and southern New Zealand and a subspecies (*E. m. novaehollandiae*) occurs on the islands off the south-east and south-west coasts of Australia, the continental coast north to Sydney, and in New Zealand on North Island and the northern tip of South Island. It pursues small fish underwater and is an extremely fast swimmer and an agile diver. The nest is built of seaweed and dry grass at the end of a burrow, or sometimes in a natural cavity. These birds nest in colonies called rookeries and when they have fledglings in the nest do their fishing in very large groups at night or evening.

A now-famous event on Philip Island in Victoria is the evening parade of these birds as they return in hordes from their fishing trips to take food to the young. This has become a tourist attraction and thousands of people visit the site every year where, under large floodlights, they can see the birds scrambling up the beach. The whole area is now, fortunately, well protected but earlier the birds were much harrassed by tourists who pulled the young from their burrows and trampled on the nests.

The Swamphen

A bird inhabiting swamps and backwaters is the Swamphen or Pukeko (*Porphyrio porphyrio*), of which there are two distinct races in Australia. The eastern or Kimberley race (*P. p.*

melanotus) is found on many of the islands, including Tasmania, and the whole of New Zealand and Australia apart from the western part south of the Fortescue River. The western Swamphen (*P. p. bellus*) is restricted to south-western Australia from Moora to Esperance. The two races have been considered as separate species in the past but are now regarded as one.

This is a large bird, about twenty inches or more in length. It usually nests in rushes just above water. It constructs its nest by bending rushes over towards the centre of what will be the nest and adding more rushes which it has bitten off. Eventually a shallow saucer shape is obtained in which the bird lays its eggs. The Swamphen has a loud, startling call which it usually utters at night or when surprised.

The Spotted Shag (*Phalacrocorax punctatus*). This handsome, fish-eating cormorant breeds in colonies on cliffs in New Zealand

Swamphen or Pukeko

(*Left*) Kiwi compared with snipe to show unique placement of kiwi's nostrils at tip of bill. The kiwi has often figured on New Zealand's stamps and coins.

The kiwis

There are three species of kiwi, the Common Kiwi (*Apteryx australis*), the Great Spotted Kiwi (*Apteryx haastii*) and the Little Spotted Kiwi (*Apteryx oweni*). Kiwis have a number of primitive and unusual features, such as solid bones with no air spaces, instead of the hollow light bones of other birds. Also, other living birds have their nostrils located close to the base of the bill, whereas the kiwi's nostrils are at the very tip of the bill. This position is probably related to the feeding habits of the kiwi, as it uses its sense of smell to locate crawling insects, ground larvae and worms in the loose soil. This is unusual in itself, as other birds rely on sight and sound more than smell to locate their food; but the kiwi has well-developed turbinal bones – the bones that support the delicate sensory membranes used to detect odours. Other primitive features of the kiwi are its rudimentary, non-functional wings and its lack of a tail.

The kiwi lives in dense forest and is active only at night, so it is very rarely seen in the wild. By day it sleeps in a small burrow. The kiwi's egg is one of the largest in the bird world in relation to the bird's size. The incubation is carried out by the male.

The giant moas

This book is concerned with living animals, but the enormous moas (family Dinorthidae) of New Zealand were such interesting animals and became extinct such a relatively short while ago that they deserve a mention here. When bird groups started to develop on islands with no mammalian predators, they often evolved into extremely large species. Later on when new factors were introduced into their islands, such as the presence of man and his domestic animals, these great birds were unable to cope and rapidly became extinct. Maori legends suggest that their forefathers, or perhaps a race of men who were in New Zealand before them, hunted and ate the moas. Modern methods of dating fossils, and the discovery of moa bones in old kitchen middens, support the idea that large moas were still living in New Zealand until 700 years ago, and smaller species until more recently.

The Giant Moa stood nearly 13 feet tall.

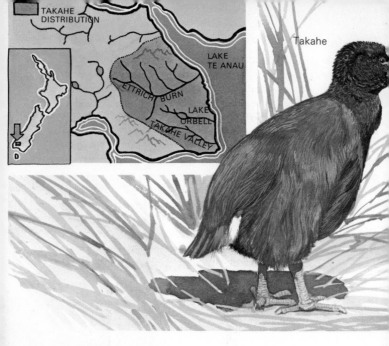

TAKAHE
DISTRIBUTION

LAKE
TE ANAU

ETTRICH BURN

LAKE
ORBELL

TAKAHE VALLEY

D

Takahe

The Takahe

When species of birds have evolved on islands where there
are no predators, they have often come down from the trees
and taken to living on the ground, and have sometimes lost
the power of flight as a result. Many members of the rail and
water-hen family have taken up this mode of life, and have
become extremely vulnerable to extinction because of the
activities of man and his efficient co-predators such as dogs,
cats, rats and mice. In modern times, the existence on small
and hitherto undisturbed oceanic islands of a number of
species in this family has become threatened by the establish-
ment of jetliner and military plane refuelling bases.

The Takahe (*Notornis hochstetteri*) is a species of water-
hen which had been described from only four known specimens before 1900. As its bones were often found associated
with those of the moas, and as it was a flightless species and
thus very susceptible to predatory pressures, it was considered to be completely extinct. One of the great ornitho-

Weka

logical sensations of this century occurred when the Takahe was discovered alive in 1948. It was found in a remote glacial valley high in the Murchison Range above Lake Te Anau (see map), where its survival was almost certainly the result of the inaccessibility of the area. It is probably still the rarest bird in the world, as less than a hundred individuals are thought to be alive, in one or two colonies. Unfortunately, the existence of the species is still very precarious, because for reasons not fully understood many of the eggs laid have proved to be infertile. This has resulted in a low rate of recruitment and a consequent danger of extinction.

The Weka

An exception to prove the rule about the susceptibility of flightless birds to extinction under pressure from predators is that of the New Zealand Weka (*Gallirallus australis*). Another flightless member of the rail family, this species has itself become a predator, feeding on rats, mice, nestling birds and the eggs of other ground-nesting birds. In this way the species has not been so affected by introduced predators and it is thus relatively common. The Weka is a nocturnal bird that lives in densely forested country and sleeps during the daytime in a burrow.

Bowerbirds

The breeding behaviour of many birds is associated with the defence, usually by the cock bird, of a particular area of ground known as a territory. Inside the territory the male advertises himself to all and sundry by prolonged calls and by displays of brilliant plumage. In a sense, this display of song and colour is a sexual characteristic, because it attracts the females of the species as well as discouraging other males. In one group of birds, the bowerbirds of Australia and New Guinea, the males are relatively inconspicuous and have developed instead an alternative feature of bright colour and attractiveness in their territory, namely the bower.

There are many species in the bowerbird family and they build bowers of varying complexity which seem to relate to the degree of the bower's importance in the mating system of the species. The simplest arrangement is the flat platform built by the bowerbirds of the genus *Archboldia* and decorated with snail shells and other objects. The next stage is that of the maypole builders such as the Golden Bowerbird (*Prionodura newtoniana*). This bird weaves vegetation round

Golden Bowerbird

Satin Bowerbird

a small sapling and decorates it with brightly coloured beetles' wings, flowers and fruits. Finally there are the true bower, or avenue, builders; these make small open tunnels of woven grass and sticks which they decorate profusely.

The Satin Bowerbird (*Ptilonorhynchus violaceus*), like the others, starts to make his bower before the female is in breeding condition. Having made this complicated structure he then proceeds to collect a multitude of objects such as flowers, fruits, feathers, bits of glass, paper, lichens, and so on, all of which are either blue or yellow in colour. It is thought that these colours are chosen because they are the same colours as the eyes and bill of rival males. These objects are either tossed around or endlessly placed and replaced while the bower is made and remade until such time as the female is ready to mate. She then takes a great interest in the bower and the male may even 'paint' the inside of the tunnel with juices from the mouth blackened by chewing burnt tree bark, fruit or wood pulp. After this stage the male removes his attention from the bower and turns it to the female, who is now receptive, and mating takes place.

The Mallee Fowl

The temperature at which eggs develop must be carefully controlled within narrow limits if the embryo is to survive to hatching. Most birds keep their eggs at the right temperature by sitting on them and keeping them close to their warm bodies. However, one family of birds, the Megapodidae, have forsaken this method and instead lay their eggs inside large artificial mounds of rotting vegetation which heat up and thus keep the eggs warm.

One species in this group, the Mallee Fowl (*Leipoa ocellata*), which lives in the central drier areas of Australia, has been extensively studied with the intention of discovering exactly how the temperature is controlled in these mounds. In autumn the male digs a crater in the ground about three feet deep; he spends all winter scratching leaves and twigs into this crater until he has a mound about one foot above ground level. During the process the vegetable matter becomes wet with the winter rains. Next the male makes a hole in the top of the vegetation which he fills with loose sand to form an egg chamber. The whole mound is then covered with loose sandy soil and smoothed over. As the wet vegetation begins to rot and ferment the internal temperature rises. When the temperature is correct in the egg chamber, the female (which often helps the male make the nest) starts to

Mallee Fowl

lay between fourteen and twenty eggs in the chamber. This takes at least five months, and as the incubation of the eggs starts immediately they are laid this means that the chicks hatch out over a similar period. Once hatching is complete it is time for the hard-working male to start another mound in preparation for the next season.

Observations have shown that the exact temperature of the mound is completely controlled by the activities of the male, who periodically tests the temperature by taking a beakful of sand from the egg chamber. During spring the vegetation is very hot so that the male's main problem is to lower the egg chamber temperature. This he does by replacing the hot sand every now and then with cool sand from beside the mound. During the summer the vegetation heat is reducing but the sand at the top of the mound is now being heated too much by the sun. Under these conditions the male replaces the hot sand with cool sand at night. In autumn the problem is reversed as there is now no heat from the mound and less from the sun. At this time the male exposes the eggs so that there is only a thin layer of sand between them and the sun. He also effectively collects heat by scratching the warm surface sand over the eggs themselves. Thus by juggling the various sources of heat the continually active male Mallee Fowl is successful in maintaining the eggs at an even temperature.

Cross-section of Mallee Fowl nest.

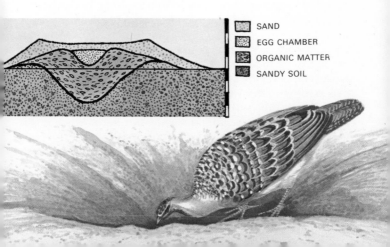

SAND
EGG CHAMBER
ORGANIC MATTER
SANDY SOIL

Noisy Scrub-bird

Rufous Scrub-bird

Scrub-birds

There are two species in this unique family (Atrichornithidae) and both are found only in small and discrete localities in Australia. They are practically flightless and closely related to the lyrebirds. The scrub-birds have strong muscular legs which they use to scratch up insects, worms and seeds. Although extremely cryptic in colouring, they have fantastic voices making loud and prolonged calls. The Rufous Scrub-bird (*Atrichornis rufescens*) is found only in Lamington National Park in Victoria. It makes a tiny domed nest near the ground, well hidden and carefully lined with soft decayed wood chewed into a sort of cardboard-like substance and plastered on the inside walls. The Noisy Scrub-bird (*Atrichornis clamosus*) was believed to be completely extinct and caused a minor sensation among bird lovers when it was rediscovered as recently as 1960 in the south-west of Western Australia. Although since then the species call has been heard by a number of people, it is such a secretive bird and so difficult to locate that only a very few have ever seen it.

Wattled Crow or Kokako

Saddleback

Wattlebirds

This family, the Callaeidae, of only two extant but rare birds is a primitive one and is believed to be closely related to the ancestors of the bowerbirds, birds of paradise and mudnest builders. They are only found on some offshore islands of New Zealand, in stands of heavily forested country where stretches of untouched vegetation such as kauri and tree ferns can be found. Wattlebirds are poor flyers, and flit or hop from branch to branch seeking insects and the flowers that they eat. The two living species are the Wattled Crow or Kokako (*Callaeus cinerea*) and the Saddleback (*Philosturnus carunculatus*).

An extinct species, last seen in 1907, called the Huia (*Heteralocha acutirostris*) was apparently unique among birds in that the male had a heavy straight beak while the female's was slighter and more curved. Both were grub eaters but the male obtained his food by chipping away at hard wood while the female probed for hers in the soft rotten wood of dead branches.

The Southern Short-nosed Bandicoot, a typical Australian marsupial mammal, has a backward-opening pouch.

MAMMALS

Characteristics

The female mammal has mammary or milk-producing glands with which she suckles her young. Mammals have a body covering of hair. Although this is greatly reduced in some, such as whales, it is generally obvious in others such as gorillas. The hairs may be modified into other sorts of external structures, such as the spines of the hedgehog or horns of the rhinoceros. Mammals (like the birds, but like no other group) are homeothermic, which means that whatever the external temperature, they keep their blood temperature within certain narrow limits. The chest and the abdomen are divided by a muscular partition called the diaphragm. The large artery which leaves the heart is located on the left side of the body and not on the right as in birds.

The mammals as a class are divided into three main groups, the monotremes, marsupials and placentals, the first two of which are largely or entirely distributed in Australia. These three groups are divided by a number of characters, most of which are concerned with the anatomy and function of the reproductive system, which are shown on pages 90 and 91 . However there are other dividing characters which are shown here.

(*Left*) Placental (Dingo) and (*right*) marsupial (Thylacine) lower jaw, left half, both seen from behind. In the marsupial lower jaw, the lower edge of the bone is characteristically bent inwards.

Monotreme (Platypus) brain, right half. The bonds linking the right and left sides (hemispheres) of the brain are one indication of development. The monotreme brain is comparatively simply organized with few bonds (shown in dark red) linking the two sides.

Marsupial (wallaby) brain, right half. This shows more linkage between the hemispheres than does the monotreme brain, but is not as advanced as the placental brain.

Corpus callosum

Placental (cat) brain, right half. A large bundle of nerve fibres, the *corpus callosum*, links the hemispheres. The brain is larger in comparison with the animal's size than is the case with the marsupials and monotremes.

Reproduction in monotremes, marsupials and placentals

Monotremes' genital tracts are completely separate for the whole of their length. They open into a common chamber with the outlet to the urinary system, which in turn opens into a common chamber with the end of the intestine. This chamber is called the *cloaca*.

BLADDER
KIDN
OVARY
INTESTINE
CLOACA

Marsupials' genital ducts are more specialized, one section being adapted to nurture the early stages of the embryo. This is called the uterus. Each side is separate but the sides sometimes form a double central vagina. The genital ducts and urinary ducts open into a common opening. The ducts from the kidneys pass *between* the genital ducts.

OVARY
KIDNEY
BLADD
UTERUS
OVIDUCT
LATERA
VAGIN
INTESTINE
CLOACA

Placentals' genital ducts are even more specialized. They are united to form a common vagina but the uteri are usually separate. The urinary ducts open into a completely separate bladder and external opening. The ducts from the kidneys pass *on each side* of the genital ducts.

KIDNE
OVARY
FALLOPI
TU
UTERUS
BLADDER
VULVA

Monotreme young are hatched from an egg laid by the mother and incubated in a pouch. The pouch is temporary and only develops when needed. The young hatch in an immature state after a short period of development and spend a long time in the pouch.

Monotremes' mammary glands are located in diffuse patches under the ventral body wall. They open to the outside through multiple enlarged pores. There are no nipples.

Marsupial embryos develop in the early stages in the uterus. The young are born through the vagina in a very immature state with no hair, no eyes, limb buds only, and no true skin. They crawl into the pouch and attach to a nipple. The development is completed in the pouch. Pregnancy is very short.

Marsupials have discrete and definite mammary glands. The nipples are well developed and when in use are very elongated.

Placental young develop in the uterus, nourished through the placenta. They are born in a well developed state, usually with hair. They are suckled at regular intervals by the mother but do not attach to the nipple. There is no pouch. Pregnancy is longer.

Placentals have definite mammary glands with nipples not so well developed.

91

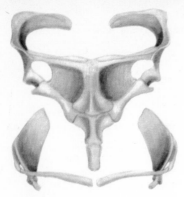

Monotreme shoulder girdle with human shoulder girdle (*below*) for comparison

Monotreme pelvic girdle. At the top are the epipubic bones found only in monotremes and marsupials.

The monotremes

Both mammals and birds evolved from a reptilian ancestor many millions of years ago. The monotremes are the mammals most closely related to that primitive ancestor, and they have retained a number of interesting structural features in their bodies which point to their past ancestry. The tabulation below lists those features found in monotremes which have been derived from their reptilian ancestry, and those which are the result of their mammalian development.

Reptilian characters

1 Monotremes have a *cloaca* – a common opening into which the end of the intestine and the urinary and genital ducts all lead.

2 They have a forelimb girdle which is very similar to that of the reptiles in that the limbs are held horizontally from the body wall before bending at the elbow or knee. This differs from the mammalian arrangement where the limbs are held vertically from the body and the elbow or knee is not normally bent. As a result of this stance the various bones of the monotreme's girdle are similar to those found in reptiles.

3 They have a number of special bones (the *prevomers* and *pterygoids*) in the skull which are not found in mammals but are found in reptiles.

4 They lay eggs containing a large amount of yolk.

Platypus skull

Echidna skull

Platypus eggs.
The mother hugs the
eggs close to her so
that the eggs frequently
become stuck together.

Mammalian characters

1 Monotremes have hair instead of scales.

2 They have mammary glands.

3 They have a heart consisting of four completely separate chambers, unlike the reptiles, some of which have partially connected anterior chambers. The large artery which leaves the heart bends to the left side instead of splitting into two branches on either side as in the reptiles.

4 The lower jaw is made up of only one bone whereas that of the reptiles is made up of several.

5 The ear has three tiny bones, the auditory ossicles, to transfer the sound from the eardrum to the actual sense organ.

6 The body temperature is regulated within definite limits, although not as efficiently as in the case of the other mammals and birds.

The picture of these ancestral characters is complicated by the fact that the living forms of monotreme, on which these characters are determined, are in fact extremely specialized to their own way of life. Therefore features such as the Platypus' loss of teeth, and the special mouth structure of the echidnas are not primitive but result merely from the animals' special functions.

The echidnas or spiny anteaters

Despite their primitive origins, the echidnas are relatively common in the less agriculturally developed areas of Australia. There are two species in Australia, the Australian Spiny Anteater (*Tachyglossus aculeatus*) and the Tasmanian Spiny Anteater (*Tachyglossus setosus*). They are active mainly in the late evening or early morning and may be seen slowly waddling along, or heard as they turn over stones to get at the ants underneath. Once a nest or trail of ants has been located, the echidna brings into use its long and sticky tongue which shoots in and out of its narrow snout, collecting a number of ants each time. Echidnas live in relatively open or scrubby country and are particularly fond of rocky and stony areas. Their coat of spines forms an excellent protection against any marauding dog and, like the hedgehog, they will immediately roll themselves up into a ball if disturbed. Another means of defence is for the animal to wedge itself into a crevice in the rocks or to grasp the ground very firmly with its exceedingly strong fore and hind limbs. Indeed, if the ground is soft enough the echidna will proceed to dig itself down vertically, keeping all its spines erect until it disappears beneath the surface of the soil – a very effective

An echidna of the genus *Tachyglossus*, showing the egg pouch.

means of retreat. The echidna has an extra long second toe with an elongated and curved nail which enables it to scratch effectively between its spines and thus to keep its skin free of parasites.

The female echidna does not build a tunnel or nest to look after its young as does the Platypus. The egg is carried in the pouch until it hatches out and the young echidna is then carried in the temporary pouch until its tiny spines start to erupt through the skin and cause discomfort to the mother. From then on the young are kept by the mother in some discreet hiding place to which she returns regularly to feed them. Echnidnas have the reptile-like ability to fast for astonishingly long periods and they may undergo a form of hibernation in very cold weather.

There is another genus of echidnas which are only found in New Guinea. A *Zaglossus* species can be distinguished from its Australian cousin by its much longer tapering muzzle which has a downward bend in it. A larger and heavier animal, it has thick black hair on its back which partially conceals its white spines.

The second claw (*left*) of the echidna's hind foot is elongated to enable it to scratch between its spines. (*Right*) The *Zaglossus* species have a longer, tapering muzzle. (*Below*) *Tachyglossus*

The Platypus female feeds her young on milk which exudes from enlarged pores rather than nipples.

The Duck-billed Platypus

When the first skins of the Platypus (*Ornithorhynchus anatinus*) reached zoologists in Europe in the late eighteenth century, many flatly refused to believe that such an animal with a duck's beak, a beaver's tail and a poisonous claw on its hind feet, really existed. They thought that the skins were fakes made up by unscrupulous taxidermists, and it was not until complete specimens arrived in 1802 that they believed in its existence. A tremendous controversy raged during that century as to whether or not the Platypus actually laid eggs, and the matter was not finally settled until 1884 when an English zoologist found eggs in the cloaca of a Platypus near the Burnett River in Queensland.

The Platypus is an aquatic beast which lives in lakes, rivers and streams from Queensland to Tasmania. As well as the flattened tail and webbed feet, the Platypus has other features well adapted for its watery life. The eyes and ears can be shut within a facial furrow when the animal is submerged. The bill has sensitive nerve endings in its tip which help the Platypus locate its food of worms and small prawns as it nuzzles through the mud at the bottom of streams. In captiv-

The Platypus' nesting burrow has a long tunnel with the entrance above water level. The female blocks the tunnel at several points when she withdraws to incubate the eggs.

ity, Platypuses eat astonishingly large quantities of food, one lactating female which weighed about two pounds consuming nearly her own weight (one and three-quarter pounds) of worms in one night.

Normally the Platypus makes a tunnel in the river bank with several openings close to the water level, usually under the roots of a tree. However, in the breeding season the female makes a special long burrow with its opening above the water level. This has an entrance tunnel over fifteen feet long which leads to the nesting chamber. When the female is about to lay her eggs, she moves back into this tunnel, plugging it at several points behind her. She lays from one to three eggs and incubates them continually for a week. When the young are hatched, the mother holds them against her underbelly where they suck the fur and cause milk to flow from the diffuse mammary glands. The young lick the milk from the skin or fur surface. After a short while the mother leaves the tunnel, but she frequently returns to suckle the young. They stay in the nesting chamber until they are about four months old. The female may use the breeding burrow many times, adding to it each season.

At one time the Platypus was extensively hunted for its very fine and beautiful fur. This reduced the numbers very considerably but fortunately the scientific importance of the species was realised in time. It is now completely protected and there is little danger of the species dying out, though it has to contend with fishing traps in which it gets caught and drowns, and has to compete with the introduced rabbit for burrowing space.

Marsupial families

Six families of marsupials survive today in the Australian region and two more are represented in the Americas.

The Didelphids are the opossums of North, South and Central America. These are small, mainly arboreal forms.

The Dasyurids include marsupial mice, native cats, the Tasmanian Devil, numbats and the Thylacine of Australia.

The Notoryctids are a tiny group which includes only the specialized marsupial moles of Australia.

The Peramelids, the bandicoots, are a group of insectivores found in Australia.

The Caenolestids, the rat opossums of South America, are a small group of semi-aquatic omnivores.

The Phalangerids are the arboreal possums, cuscuses, and Koala of Australia.

The Vombatids are the wombats of Australia.

The Macropodids are the kangaroos and wallabies, rat kangaroos and tree kangaroos of Australia. They are true herbivores with teeth modified to cut and chew vegetation.

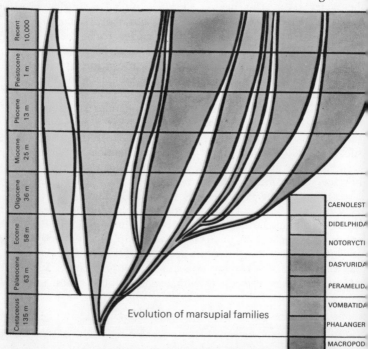

Evolution of marsupial families

Recent 10,000	
Pleistocene 1 m	
Pliocene 13 m	
Miocene 25 m	
Oligocene 36 m	CAENOLEST
Eocene 58 m	DIDELPHIDA
	NOTORYCTI
Palaeocene 63 m	DASYURIDA
	PERAMELID
Cretaceous 135 m	VOMBATIDA
	PHALANGER
	MACROPOD

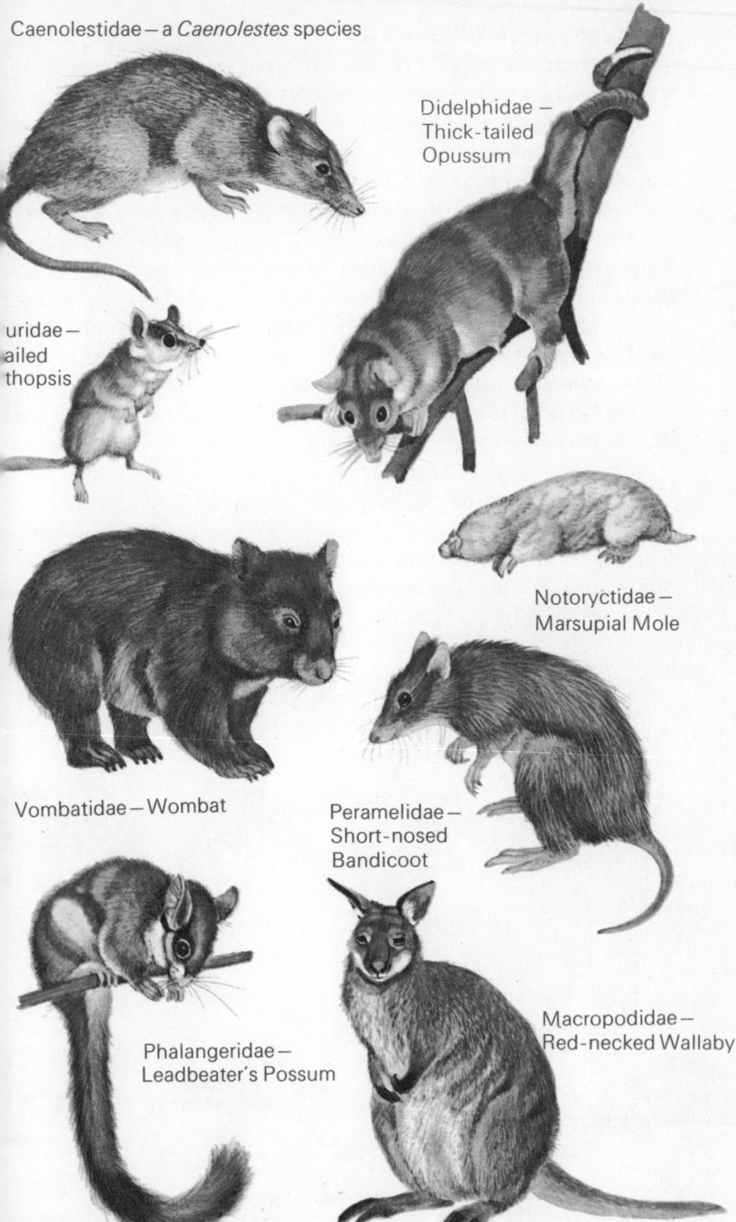

Caenolestidae — a *Caenolestes* species

Didelphidae —
Thick-tailed
Opussum

...uridae —
...ailed
...thopsis

Notoryctidae —
Marsupial Mole

Vombatidae — Wombat

Peramelidae —
Short-nosed
Bandicoot

Phalangeridae —
Leadbeater's Possum

Macropodidae —
Red-necked Wallaby

Convergence of marsupials and placentals

In any community of animals, different species tend to have different roles in the total utilization of the available food and other resources. Biologists refer to the place an animal takes in this interrelated community as its *niche*. When a group of animals is successful in evolution and starts to diversify into many different species, each species will take on a different role or, in other words, fill a different niche. If different basic groups of animals occupy separate continents, the body shape and way of functioning of species in comparable niches tends to be remarkably similar even though their evolutionary origins may be completely different. This phenomenon is called *convergence* and by far the best example of it is found in the astonishing similarity between many of the Australian marsupials and placentals which fill similar niches in different parts of the world.

The Thylacine or Marsupial Wolf is almost identical in body shape to the placental wolf of the northern hemisphere. The marsupial mole, though a different colour, is identical in shape to its placental counterpart. The wombat is very similar in shape to the marmot; and many other examples can be

MARSUPIAL MOLE   THYLACINE   NATIVE CAT   WOMBA

MOLE   WOLF   CIVET   COYPU

given (see illustration). In other cases, although the body shape may not be similar, the similar way of life is reflected in the internal functions of the body. For example, although the kangaroos do not look like deer or cattle, they have almost identical stomach structures, and recent research has shown that the way in which they digest the grass they eat, with the help of stomach bacteria and protozoans, is very similar to the method of digestion in their placental associates. Thus convergence shows very clearly that the shape of an animal and the way it functions are very largely determined by the type of niche it fills.

When the marsupial group started to diversify in the empty continent of Australia, they tended to fill every available niche with a marsupial representative. There are two niches which were not available to marsupials. Firstly there are no aerial or flying marsupials because the only placental group which was able to get to Australia when the marsupials were evolving were the bats which thus filled this type of niche. Secondly there are no aquatic marsupials in Australia. This was because a monotreme, the Platypus, had already filled the stream and lake dwelling mammalian niche.

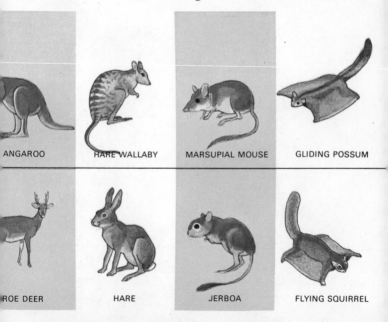

ANGAROO   HARE WALLABY   MARSUPIAL MOUSE   GLIDING POSSUM

ROE DEER   HARE   JERBOA   FLYING SQUIRREL

The Koala

The Koala (*Phascolarctos cinereus*) is as zoologically interesting as it is attractive. It is thought to be closely related to the wombat. It has pockets in the mouth to store and carry food, has a backward-opening pouch, and also lacks a tail – all of which are features of the wombat. Apparently both animals diverged from a ground living ancestor, the Koala evolving to an arboreal niche while the wombat took to a more fossorial or underground existence. Koalas are well known for the extreme specialization of their feeding habits. They will only eat the tips of young leaves of certain species of gum tree, and so their range is closely limited by the range of distribution of these trees. To aid in the digestion of this peculiar diet, they have a very modified digestive tract, one feature of which is the large caecum to deal with their average intake of about two and a half pounds of leaves per day. It is thought that digestion also involves certain special bacteria which live in the gut. When the young Koala is just being weaned from its mother's milk she produces a special sort of faecal

The Koala eats the leaves of certain species of gum tree. The young cling to the mother's back (*left*) after leaving the pouch.

dropping – a green pap which the young one eats. As well as helping the young Koala's digestion with partially digested food, this method of feeding probably serves also to introduce into the intestine the special bacteria required for digestion.

The baby Koala is born after a pregnancy of about thirty-five days and then goes into the pouch. For a considerable time after leaving the pouch, the young are closely associated with the mother, and they can be seen clinging cheerfully to her back as she sits in the gum trees feeding on leaves. Although the Koala is much loved today, there was a time not so many years ago when, due to very intensive shooting and trapping for its skin, the species came near to extinction. In addition, the Koala seems more susceptible than many other wild mammals to epidemic diseases. Fortunately the species is now completely protected and much good work has been done by State fauna authorities, notably in Victoria, to reintroduce Koalas into areas where they had become extinct.

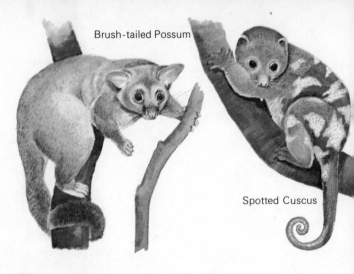

Brush-tailed Possum

Spotted Cuscus

The possums

The Phalangeridae are a very widespread and successful group of marsupials, being found in their tree habitat all over Australia and New Guinea, and one species is now even living successfully, perhaps too successfully, in New Zealand.

The Brush-tailed Possum (*Trichosurus vulpecula*) is probably the commonest marsupial in Australia. It occurs in very considerable numbers all over the southern and eastern sides of the continent, and has been least affected in its numbers by the spread of agricultural development or other human interference. Indeed, the Brush-tail has become a considerable pest in many suburbs, as it has taken to nesting in houses in the space between the ceiling and the roof, causing considerable annoyance by its noisy fighting and plentiful urination. The Brush-tail normally nests or sleeps in the hollows of trees but may occasionally sleep in rabbit warrens.

The diet of the Brush-tail is a wide one as it will eat many sorts of leaves and buds and will also feed on carrion. The individuals are very aggressive to each other, especially the males. The young are born after only seventeen days gestation but they remain in the pouch for another four months. If the baby is lost at birth the female will mate again and imme-

Long-fingered Striped Possum

Common Ring-tailed Possum

diately start another pregnancy, although normally only one baby is produced each year.

The Brush-tail was once much in demand for fur, at least four million skins being marketed in 1906. Between 1858 and 1920 over 600 Brush-tails were liberated at four different localities in New Zealand, and it has become a considerable pest there. Many of the local trees have been unable to recover from severe defoliation caused by these possums. Here is an excellent example of the interrelationships of animals and plants. This possum had evolved in Australia along with the trees it fed on, with the result that both plant and animal were well adjusted to each other. However, the tree species in New Zealand are not of a type that could stand heavy use by a herbivore, and as a result many trees are dying or dead because of the activities of the Brush-tail.

The Pygmy or Feathertail Glider (*Acrobates pygmaeus*) is a delicate and very attractive little marsupial which has special membranes on either side of its body between the front and hind legs. These when spread out act as vanes to allow the animal to take great gliding leaps from branch to branch. This means of getting about is called volplaning and the tiny tail is used as a sort of aerial rudder to guide the glider as it leaps. Active at night and quite torpid during the day, the

Pygmy Glider feeds mainly on insects, although termites and occasionally nectar are eaten. It builds a small nest of globular shape made of gum leaves in a hollow limb. There are four teats in the pouch, and as happens with some other marsupials, more than four young are often born but the extra ones die as they cannot attach themselves to a teat.

The Greater Glider Possum (*Schoinobates volans*) is a much larger glider and is quite common in the eastern States. There is a very wide range of coat colours in this species depending on the position in the range of distribution. Greater Gliders are particularly clumsy on the ground and when they do come down from the trees they easily fall prey to foxes and other carnivores. In the trees, however, they are really in their element, and they hold all Australian records for gliding species. One animal was recorded as covering 500 yards in a total of six glides.

The Greater Glider is almost entirely a vegetarian, eating only leaf tips and flower blossoms. It can be seen fairly easily at night with the aid of torchlight, as the eyes reflect the beam very clearly. During the day, hitting the base of a tree containing a Greater Glider's nest of bark and leaves will result in a head peering out to see what is causing the disturbance.

The Common Ring-tailed Possum (*Pseudocheirus laniginosus*) is characterized by a long tapered tail which can be curled up into a ring. This tail is used for clasping branches

Greater Glider Possum

Pygmy or Feathertail Glider

when the animal is climbing. The Ring-tail builds a large nest or 'drey' in the shape of a football, made out of inter-twined leaves and twigs. About ten inches in diameter, it has a five-inch opening to the central chamber. Although the species prefers tea trees and peppermint gums as a home, it will eat many different types of leaves and also the shoots and berries of shrubs. Its main defence against any disturbance is to 'freeze' and then creep quietly away. Its call is a very pleasant bird-like note which is repeated several times.

The Spotted Cuscus (*Phalanger maculatus*) is a native of the tropical forests of New Guinea, Papua and the Cape York district of Queensland. A very slow moving and sluggish animal, it has a way of life very similar to the lorises. Active at night it is mainly a leaf eater but despite its slow move-ments it can also catch and eat small birds and mammals. The northern male animals are spotted but the females have an even coat.

The Long-fingered Striped Possum (*Dactylonax palpator*) is a brightly striped species which is found only in New Guinea and Papua. It shows another striking example of convergence, as it has one particularly long thin finger in each hand which is used to extract the larvae of certain wood-boring beetles which live in tunnels in wood. An exactly similar modification of the hand is found in the Aye-aye of Malagasy, a primate which feeds on similar wood-boring grubs.

Greater Glider Possum in flight

The Honey Possum's tongue has bristles on the end, an adaptation enabling it to feed on nectar from flowers.

The Honey Possum (*Tarsipes spencerae*) is a good example of ultra-specialization to a specific food source. This species is found only in the south-west of Western Australia. It has an extremely long snout and a tongue with bristles just like the honeyeaters (see page 72). It feeds on nectar from flowers, probing with its tongue and then withdrawing it into the mouth where special ridges on the roof of the mouth scrape the food off. The teeth are small and degenerate.

Honey Possums often travel in pairs, moving from one flowering plant to another. They make a little nest of grass and fur and often locate this in deserted birds' nests or under the 'skirt' of blackboys or grass trees. They will occasionally eat insects, especially night-flying moths.

Marsupial Mole

The Marsupial Mole

The burrowing mode of life of the Marsupial Mole (*Notoryctes typhlops*) has led to an overall conformation very similar to its placental counterparts the moles. It is about seven inches long. The snout has a protective horny shield and there are no eyes and no external ear lobes. The pouch opens backwards and the limbs are particularly short and strong with much enlarged nails on the digits to help in the digging action of the limbs. The fur is very fine, almost iridescent, and ranges in colour from almost white to golden-red.

The Marsupial Mole is found only in desert areas of central Australia and it is rarely collected as it seems to spend practically its whole life underground. After the rare rains of the interior, however, it will come to the surface and it can be tracked at this time. The Marsupial Mole does not make permanent tunnels through the sand but burrows along a few inches under the surface for long distances. Its main diet is worms, which it eats in very considerable quantities.

A related species, the North-western Marsupial Mole (*Notoryctes caurinus*) has only been described from a very few specimens collected in the north-west of Western Australia. It is slightly smaller than the Marsupial Mole, has a shorter muzzle and different dentition.

The Numbat or Banded Anteater

The family of carnivorous marsupials (Dasyuridae) consists of four subfamilies: the Myrmecobiinae which includes the Numbat and Rusty Numbat; the Phascogalinae or marsupial

109

Numbat or Banded Anteater

mice; the Dasyurinae, which includes the native cats and the Tasmanian Devil; and the Thylacininae, the only representative of which is the Thylacine.

Most of the smaller marsupials are creatures of the night, sleeping the day away in a secluded burrow, log or branch. Not so the Numbat (*Myrmecobius fasciatus*) which is active during the daylight hours. The species feeds almost exclusively on ants and termites and has a narrow snout with a thin tongue which can be protruded several inches to capture its prey. Because of its diet, the Numbat's teeth are very small and degenerate, as they are little used in crushing the termites; but astonishingly, there are an enormous number of them. The teeth vary from fifty to fifty-two, which is the largest number found in land mammals.

The Numbat is generally a solitary animal, living in open eucalypt forest where the undergrowth consists of small shrubs. It is particularly fond of forests of Wandoo (*Eucalyptus redunca*), the floor of which is characterized by many fallen tree trunks and branches which have been hollowed out by the activities of termites. The Numbat uses these hollow limbs as cover into which it runs if disturbed.

However, if the observer remains very quiet and motionless, the beautifully marked head and body of the Numbat will slowly emerge from a tree limb, and off the animal will go, sniffing the ground in search of new termite nests on which to feed. Once a nest is located, the Numbat digs it up with its forefeet and sits there licking up the exposed termites.

The female Numbat has no pouch in which the young can complete their development, but instead they hold on to the mother's teat and grip the hair of her belly. When they are very small, they become permanently attached to the teat for a time – like many other marsupials – because the end of the teat swells inside the mouth cavity and the young Numbat's lips seal around the shaft of the teat so that it cannot be extracted without damaging the lips. Normally four young are born at a time.

Numbats frequent Wandoo forests, where fallen trees provide cover

The Tasmanian Devil

The Tasmanian Devil (*Sarcophilus harrisi*) is a small stocky animal about the size of a cocker spaniel, but with a very powerful head and disproportionately large forequarters. It has massive and strong teeth which are used for crushing bones and can thus inflict a very severe bite if the animal is molested. The Devil lives in scrub or rocky country in Tasmania. It is a carnivore and feeds on any type of meat or carrion it can get. Its normal diet includes scrub wallabies, rats, birds, lizards, snakes, possums, cats and rabbits. An interesting feature of the Devil's method of eating is that it devours its prey whole, including the skin and bones. It seems likely that the Tasmanian Devil evolved to fill the same type of niche as the hyaena of Africa, that of a scavenger which follows large predators, in this case probably the Thylacine (see page 114), and feeds on the remnants of carcasses left behind. It is not a very swift-moving animal and has a peculiar slow shuffling gait. The males particularly are very aggressive to each other and make a tremendous amount of

The carnivorous Tasmanian Devil inhabits scrub and rocky country.

noise when they fight as the contest seems mainly to consist of snarling and screaming.

The Tasmanian Devil breeds in March and after a gestation period of thirty-one days a litter of three or four young are born. The mother's pouch opens backwards, and by the time the young are ten weeks old they are hanging out of the pouch although still attached to the teat. At fifteen weeks they are off the nipple but they grow relatively slowly, being only half grown the next breeding season when a new litter is born. This suggests that the young Devils do not breed until they are in their second year.

The Tasmanian Devil was persecuted by early settlers because it stole chickens and it is now found only in the remoter parts of Tasmania, although it is not in any danger of extinction.

The Thylacine or Marsupial Wolf

There is still a great deal of controversy among Australian biologists and conservationists over whether or not this species of large wolf-like carnivorous marsupial is still extant. Because of its habit of killing the holiest animal on the Australian scene, the sheep, the Thylacine (*Thylacinus cynocephalus*) was very extensively hunted in Tasmania throughout the last century. Its habitat in thickly wooded upland country has also been greatly altered by agricultural development. As a result the species was already very rare by the end of the nineteenth century and since then there have been a number of expeditions to determine if the species still survives in the wild and heavily wooded country of north-western Tasmania. The last known wild specimen was shot in 1930; the last live one in captivity died in Hobart Zoo in 1933. However, evidence from tracks in 1957 and from the blood and hairs found in a sprung trap in 1961 would suggest that a few Thylacines survive.

One of the problems in ascertaining whether Thylacines are still extant involves the difficulty in distinguishing them from the occasional feral dog. The Thylacine has pronounced stripes over the back of the body, a most un-dog-like character, and in addition the shape of the base of the tail

114

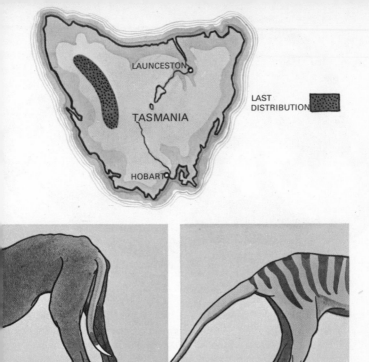

DOG

THYLACINE

The base of the Thylacine's tail (*right*) is quite differently shaped from that of a dog (*left*).

(see picture) is quite different. Because of the muscular attachment of the Thylacine's tail it cannot be wagged.

An efficient predator, the Thylacine feeds on kangaroos, wallabies and smaller marsupials. It eats only selected parts of its victim, being primarily a blood-feeder, sucking blood from the severed neck veins. It hunts at night or at dusk by jogging along after its fleeing prey and then catching it after a final burst of speed. It is normally solitary. Although the species did originally occur on the mainland as well, it was extinct there well before European settlement, possibly as the result of competition from the introduced Dingo.

Tiger Cat

The native cats

As well as the Tasmanian Devil and the Thylacine, the Dasyuridae family contains a number of smaller cat- or weasel-like forms which prey on the smaller marsupials. The species are all very similar, having almost identical types of ear and muzzle shape and with the soles of the front and back feet being very similar in shape through the whole family. The teeth are naturally all well adapted to meat diets of various types.

The Tiger Cat (*Dasyurops Maculatus*) is found in wooded country in the eastern states & Tasmania. It is a great climber and has specially modified feet with hard curved nails and serrated pads to help it grasp the trunks of trees. The Tiger Cat is a shy but ferocious animal which can grow up to four feet long. It can be distinguished from all the other native cats in that the spots present in the fur pattern continue down into the fur of the tail. Birds, rabbits, reptiles and insects are all eaten and the Tiger Cat also has a bad reputation as an occasional raider of poultry farms.

The Little Northern Native Cat (*Satanellus hallucatus*) is one of the smaller native cats. This species is found in the northern parts of Western Australia, the Northern Territory

116

and Queensland. A very primitive form, it has a number of body features which show its close relationships with the second group of the dasyurids, the marsupial mice. It is commonly found in the large rock piles which dot the northern landscape, and it feeds on small lizards and insects. Its temperament is very appropriately described by its generic name which means 'little devil'.

The Eastern Native Cat (*Dasyurus quoll*) is relatively common in the outer suburbs of many cities in the coastal regions of the eastern states. It is about eighteen inches long and has most attractive markings in the fur of its back. A very efficient nocturnal carnivore, it also has a bad reputation as a poultry killer. Like many carnivores the Eastern Native Cat kills by a single bite at the back of the head. An interesting feature of its reproduction is that the mother's pouch only develops when the young are about to be born, and although only six teats are available, up to twenty-four young are born at a time, so the majority die at birth. A very intelligent creature, it is a fearless animal and seems to be well able to withstand the persecution meted out to it by human beings.

Eastern Native Cat

Little Northern
Native Cat

Marsupial mice

Although the Phascogalinae, or marsupial mice, look like rodents, they have eight incisors in the top jaw and six in the bottom – a feature which immediately distinguishes them from the placental rodents all of which have only two incisors in the top jaw and two in the bottom. There are many species of marsupial mice distributed all over the Australian continent.

The Yellow-footed Marsupial Mouse (*Antechinus flavipes*) is especially interesting to zoologists because its skeletal structure has many features which suggest that it resembles most closely what the original or stem-form of marsupial was probably like. A fairly common animal, it is found in many parts of the continent, living in rock crevices, tree hollows, logs and caves. The feet of the Yellow-footed Marsupial Mouse have long claws and special ridged pads which aid it in climbing so that the species is very arboreal. It makes a small nest of leaves and has a wide diet of all types of insects and larvae, and will occasionally eat other small mammals such as wild house mice.

Animals have evolved many different ways of storing food inside their bodies. One of the strangest cases is the storage of fat in the tail of the Fat-tailed Sminthopsis (*Sminthopsis crassicaudata*). The thickness of the tail varies considerably with the seasons and the state of nutritional well-being of the animal. A terrestrial desert-living form, it frequents hollow logs or small burrows in the ground. Its main diet consists of

Fat-tailed Sminthopsis

Yellow-footed Marsupial Mouse

insects, mainly grasshoppers, beetles and cockroaches. Although small in size, the Fat-tailed Sminthopsis eats a very considerable quantity of food at each meal. It has up to ten young which cling on to the back of the mother as she moves about.

The Crest-tailed Marsupial Mouse or Mulgara (*Dasycercus cristicauda*) is another desert species. This attractive little creature is a very efficient killer, being able to kill domestic mice its own size with a single bite at the nape of the neck. It makes a particularly careful toilet after eating, and indeed it eats its prey in a delicate and deliberate way. The Mulgara first skins the head, which it crushes and eats, and then skins the animal backwards as it devours the body, leaving the skin more or less intact when the meal is consumed.

Like the Numbat, the Mulgara is rather unusual among the smaller marsupials in that it is active in the daytime. It carries its litter of six or seven young dangling or hanging on to the teats because the pouch is poorly developed, but despite this burden, the female Mulgara can successfully attack and kill prey with her litter attached.

The Eastern Jerboa Marsupial (*Antechinomys laniger*) is an excellent example of convergence of body form, its external shape being almost identical to that of the jerboas of Asia. Despite its miniature kangaroo-like appearance, this species has a backward-opening pouch which is extremely variable in its degree of development from one female to another. A nocturnal animal, its diet consists mainly of insects.

Crest-tailed Marsupial Mouse or Mulgara

Eastern Jerboa Marsupial

Southern Short-nosed Bandicoot

Long-nosed Bandicoot

The bandicoots

The bandicoots are a marsupial group which are not really like any type of placental mammals. They belong to the family Peramelidae all the members of which have a characteristically long and pointed snout. The group are generally nocturnal and have a varied diet, feeding on caterpillars, slugs, earthworms, snails, insects, small lizards and occasionally vegetable matter. Some members have specialized more as carnivores and eat small mammals, while others tend towards an insectivorous diet and eat termites. They dig for their food in soft soil and make a distinctive small cone-shaped hole in the ground. A few species live in rather deep burrows while others make small surface nests of grass. They all have an unusual arrangement of teats in the pouch, the nipples lying in two curved rows.

The Southern Short-nosed Bandicoot (*Isoodon obesulus*) is perhaps the commonest bandicoot. It makes a surface nest of leaves and twigs, which has no definite entrance but which

Pig-footed Bandicoot

Bilby or Rabbit-eared Bandicoot

is rebuilt each time the animal goes in and out. Although it is mainly insectivorous, it will eat mice and rats, and it plays with them before finally devouring them, in the same manner as a domestic cat.

Beetle larvae and other grubs and worms are the main items in the diet of the Long-nosed Bandicoot (*Perameles nasuta*). It is fastidious in its eating habits; before it eats the animals it catches it cleans the soil from them very carefully by brushing it off with its forefeet.

Because the first described specimen of the very rare Pig-footed Bandicoot (*Chaeropus ecaudatus*) had lost its tail, it was given a species name which means 'no tail'. Early collectors repeatedly confused their aboriginal assistants by asking them to catch the bandicoot without a tail, which was actually impossible as the species does have a small tail! The feet are unusual and reminiscent in shape of those of the ungulate placentals.

121

Common Wombat

The Bilby or Rabbit-eared Bandicoot (*Macrotis lagotis*) is another rare species. It builds a complex series of tunnels which can go deeper than five feet into the ground. It has several nests in this burrow system and feeds mainly on termites.

Wombats

These creatures are sufficiently unlike all the other Australian marsupials to be placed in a small family of their own, the Vombatidae. They are probably most closely related to the possum family and in particular the Koala (see page 102) but they have only a single pair of upper and lower incisors which have no fixed roots and grow continually. This is a most unmarsupial-like character and is similar to the normal condition of incisor teeth of placental rodents. Wombats are entirely vegetarian, feeding on grasses and the roots of shrubs and occasionally eating tree bark. They make very large burrows by lying on their side and digging with their very powerful front legs and pushing the soil back with their hind feet. Their burrows are usually more than ten feet long and have been recorded as long as 100 feet. A very small child could easily crawl along a wombat burrow to the nesting chamber.

Wombats are usually solitary animals except in the mating season which takes place in April to June. Although there are two nipples in the pouch, only a single young is born. The wombat is an inoffensive animal and makes a very good house pet. Its only noise is a sort of rather apologetic growling cough. Unfortunately it has been heavily persecuted and the Tasmanian race is now probably extinct. The Common Wombat (*Vombatus hirsutus*) is found in hilly or mountainous country in south-eastern Australia but the Hairy-nosed Wombat (*Lasiorhinus latifrons*) has now a very restricted range in South Australia. This species is smaller than the Common Wombat, which has been known to weigh as much as eighty pounds.

Wombats live in long burrows.
The Hairy-nosed Wombat
(*below*) is smaller than the
Common Wombat.

Rat kangaroos

The kangaroos all belong to the very large family Macropodidae, the name itself describing their main characteristic of very long thin feet. They all have a fairly similar body shape and a long tail which is used like an extra leg when they are moving slowly, and as a counterbalance to the body while hopping at speed. The group consists of two subfamilies, the rat kangaroos, the Potoroinae and the 'true' kangaroos and wallabies, the Macropodinae. The rat kangaroos are smaller in size and their teeth are of a type which suggests that the subfamily has not yet fully evolved away from the ancestral insectivorous type of diet to the completely herbivorous diet of the Macropodinae.

There were once many different species of the Potoroinae subfamily but they have been heavily reduced by introduced placental predators such as the Dingo, Red Fox and cat. The various species are all somewhat similar in external appearance and in their way of life. They are nocturnal and lie up during the day in grass nests made in shallow excavations and covered with debris and twigs. At night some species are singularly unafraid of man, and before their numbers so declined they would visit the campfires of many bushmen and

Brush-tailed Rat Kangaroo or Woilie

become practically 'household' pets. The rat kangaroos feed generally on grasses or root tubers and some underground fungi. They are very aggressive to each other, and males in captivity will frequently kill other males.

The Brush-tailed Rat Kangaroo or Woilie (*Bettongia penicillata*) was once one of the most common marsupial species and was found in large numbers all over the southern half of the continent. It is now rare and possibly extinct in many areas of the eastern states although it still occurs in numbers in the south-west of Western Australia. It makes nests in the hollow at the base of overhanging bushes and can carry nesting material in its prehensile tail. The Woilie was once so common in South Australia that it was used for coursing in the fashion of coursing for hares but the species is now extinct in that State.

Although now very rare on the mainland, the Long-nosed Rat Kangaroo or the Potoroo (*Potorous tridactylus*) is still common in Tasmania. It lives in swampy country and nests in very dense vegetation. The Potoroo is active during day and night. Because its hind feet are relatively short for a macropodid, it moves in a sort of ungainly galloping motion touching the ground with its forefeet as well.

Long-nosed Rat Kangaroo or Potoroo

Ring-tailed
Rock Wallaby

Banded Hare Wallaby

Brush-tailed Rock Wallaby

Wallabies

The Macropodinae are the largest group of Australian marsupials and their height when standing ranges from about two feet to over six feet. Generally the smaller members of the group are called wallabies and the larger ones kangaroos, although there is little to distinguish them from each other zoologically and their sizes can even overlap. They are found all over the Australian continent and have even spread into New Guinea and Papua. There are many different species, but most species have been greatly reduced in numbers since European settlement.

The Banded Hare Wallaby (*Lagostrophus fasciatus*) was once common in the thick scrubland near swamps along the coast of Western Australia. It is now only found on a few offshore islands. It was probably because of their banded coloration that the early English explorer and privateer,

Dama Wallaby

Crescent Nail-tail Wallaby

William Dampier, called them a sort of raccoon. These animals were extensively hunted by the aborigines who used to set the vegetation alight to drive them towards their spears.

A number of species of wallaby have become adapted to the rocky outcrops and caves which are a feature of the Australian landscape. These rock wallabies are exceptionally agile jumpers and have well padded feet. During the hottest part of the day they will lie up in the cool recesses of a rock cave but they are active at night, moving all over the rock piles like so many mountain goats. The Brush-tailed Rock Wallaby (*Petrogale penicillata*) frequents the mountainous gorges of eastern New South Wales and other States, especially in well timbered country. The Ring-tailed Rock Wallaby (*Petrogale xanthopus*) lives in more central regions of Australia, but because of its very beautiful markings it was extensively hunted for the fur trade and is now much reduced in numbers.

The Crescent Nail-tail Wallaby (*Onychogalea lunata*) is a rare species from Western Australia which has a curious horny projection on the tip of its tail the function of which is unknown. It lives on tussocky grass plains or in rocky scrubby country and has well developed claws on the forepaws which it uses for grubbing in the soil for food.

The Dutch explorer Pelsart described the Tammar or Dama Wallaby from the Houtman Albrolhos of Geraldton in Western Australia in 1629, making it the first Australian marsupial species to be known in Europe. The Tammar (*Protemnodon eugenii*) lives in thick coastal scrub where it makes small tunnel-like runways through the vegetation. It lives on rough foliage and can eat bark and leaves as well as grass and shrubs. When hopping along at its fastest, it holds its two small forefeet out sideways like paddles to act as balancing organs for the top of the body. The true manner of marsupial birth (see page 138) was first observed in a captive pet Tammar, a birth being seen and recorded by Surgeon Collie on H.M.S. *Sulphur* in 1830.

Unlike many other wallabies the Sandy or Agile Wallaby (*Protemnodon agilis*) is still to be found in great numbers in the far north of Australia where it can be seen at times in mobs near limestone hills and on creek flats. As is the case with many

Black-tailed or Swamp Wallaby

Pretty-face Wallaby

other wallabies, the female is much smaller than the male.

The Pretty-face Wallaby (*Protemnodon elegans*) is sometimes called the Whiptail as it has a very long slender tail. It is a fast moving animal and is found in small bands in tall brushwood country in Queensland and New South Wales. Despite its speed it is very curious, which makes it easy to hunt. It can frequently be observed as it lies in the shade during its midday camps.

The Black-tailed or Swamp Wallaby (*Protemnodon bicolor*) is a relatively plentiful species because it lives in a wide range of habitats. It is found in greatest numbers in swampy country where the vegetation is thick and impenetrable to predators, and in steep-sided rocky gullies of the mountainous regions of Victoria, New South Wales and Queensland.

The Black-gloved Wallaby (*Protemnodon irma*) is a fast-moving species which prefers the open scrubby bush of the south of Western Australia. Unlike the other species which tend to be browsers on shrubs and bushes, the Black-gloved Wallaby is a true grazer feeding on grasses.

Sandy or Agile Wallaby

Black-gloved Wallaby

The Quokka

The Quokka (*Setonix brachyurus*) was once very common in the swamps and thickets of the whole south coastal region of Western Australia but is now very rare on the mainland because of the clearing of its habitat for agriculture. This little wallaby survives, however, in great numbers on two islands off the coast (see map) where it has been the subject of the first modern series of ecological and physiological investigations of an Australian marsupial. The Quokka lived originally in dense *Acacia* thickets, feeding mainly on the growing shoots, but frequent burning on Rottnest Island has greatly reduced the area covered by these plants so that the animal has had to change its diet. For much of the year it feeds on other, less nutritious grasses and shrubs. There is little water on the island except for some freshwater soaks at the edge of salt lakes, and Quokkas living away from these soaks have to eat plants which, though high in water content, are particularly unnutritious, thus making the poor diet worse.

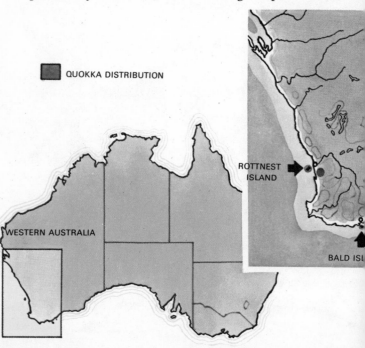

QUOKKA DISTRIBUTION

WESTERN AUSTRALIA

ROTTNEST ISLAND

BALD ISL

Quokkas drink at freshwater soaks beside salt lakes.

Quokkas are born in summer when the food supply is at its worst, but the length of development in the pouch means that the young leave the pouch and stop suckling in the winter when the food and water situation is perhaps best. Almost every adult female carries a single baby in the pouch for the first half of the year. Many young die, however, in the severe conditions which occur in the summer of their first year. In the rare mainland populations, the available diet does not alter so much and it seems that there the Quokkas breed all the year round.

A mainly nocturnal animal, the Quokka lies up in the heat of the day under shade in the *Acacia* thickets. On Rottnest Island it has become quite used to humans and near holiday cottages will forage in dustbins and backyards in search of food. The island was named by an early Dutch explorer William De Vlamingh who described the great numbers of rat-like animals there and called it by the Dutch for 'rat nest'.

131

Tree kangaroos

It is an interesting aspect of evolution that if species leave one habitat in the course of their development and then return to it later on, they cannot reverse the evolution of the body changes which have occurred during their first move, but must further modify these alterations to suit their original habitat. Like all kangaroos, the tree kangaroos are thought to have originally evolved from a possum-like tree-dwelling stock which abandoned the arboreal way of life and adapted its appendages for dwelling on the ground. This meant the loss of the clinging great toe which possums use in climbing trees, and the development of a very muscular tail which was not prehensile. When the tree kangaroos returned to a tree-dwelling existence, these features could not be restored, but instead the limbs were altered so that the fore and hind limbs are the most nearly equal in length of any of the kangaroos. The long pads on the feet are deeply serrated and are flattened to act as friction pads when the animal is climbing, and there are very long curved nails on each toe.

Tree kangaroos are found in forested regions in New

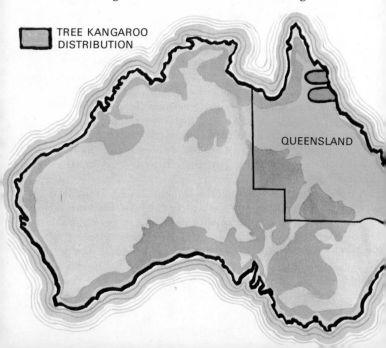

TREE KANGAROO
DISTRIBUTION

QUEENSLAND

Lumholtz's Tree Kangaroo

Guinea and in the mountainous and tableland regions of
Queensland. They are excellent climbers and can make astonishingly long downward leaps of over thirty feet. They feed
on tree leaves and ferns and are partial to native and introduced fruits. There are two species on the Australian mainland, the Dusky or Bennett's Tree Kangaroo (*Dendrolagus
bennettianus*) and Lumholtz's Tree Kangaroo (*Dendrolagus
lumholtzi*). Both species have a rather long shaggy coat. The
natural resting position of the animals is a squatting one,
unlike the rather upright stance of the other kangaroos.

Great Grey Kangaroo

The large kangaroos

In the minds of most people these animals most typify the Australian fauna. The long hopping progression of the kangaroo is one of the most graceful movements in the animal kingdom, the heavy tail swinging up and down each time the animal leaves the ground. The larger species have no difficulty in maintaining speeds of over twenty-five miles per hour. The length and height of the kangaroo's leap has been the subject of innumerable bushmen's yarns but there is no doubt that leaps of twenty-five feet are commonplace and measured leaps of up to forty feet have been reported. In height, eight feet has been cleared easily and the highest leap is reported to have been about ten and a half feet.

The many species of kangaroo can be divided into three main groups on the basis of habitat: the forest kangaroos, the plains kangaroos, and the wallaroos of the mountains and rocky country. The forest kangaroos frequent the dense and more open wooded regions of the southern parts of the con-

Wallaroo or Euro

tinent. The largest of all marsupials, they are represented by the Great Grey Kangaroo (*Macropus canguru*) of the eastern States, which is over six feet tall when fully grown. It lives in mobs of about ten to thirty animals and can move with astonishing speed through the forest. The Red Kangaroo (*Macropus rufus*) is the commonest species of kangaroo and occurs all over Australia on the open grassland plains and in open scrub. A thinner animal, its fore and hind limbs are more elongated than the Great Grey's and it has a short coat which is quite variable in colour. In eastern Australia, the males are reddish, but many females are a beautiful smoky blue-grey colour which has earned them the name of 'blue flyers'. The Red Kangaroo is a social animal and sometimes occurs in mobs of hundreds of animals, making a fascinating sight as they bound across the plains. Like all the kangaroos, the males, particularly the older ones or 'boomers' as they are called, fight on occasion, boxing each other with their forefeet and attempting to scratch the underbelly of

Red Kangaroo.
(*Opposite*) Male kangaroos fight by
rising on their tails and kicking at
each other's belly.

their opponent with their large hind feet. This species' habit
of boxing has resulted in its inclusion in many circus side-
show acts where it usually flattens human opponents with a
sweep of its very strong tail. In hilly or broken country the
Wallaroo or Euro (*Macropus robustus*) is found, a thick-set
animal with broad powerful shoulders and shorter stouter
limbs. It also has a much longer coat which in southern
regions is quite shaggy. The Euro has exceptionally broad
footpads to assist it in jumping from rock to rock over rough
country. A less social species than the other kangaroos, it is
only found in small family groups of a male, female and
perhaps her latest young. A feature of this species is its
ability to go without water for very long periods, in some
cases more than a week. Once disturbed, all the other species
of kangaroo will flee, but the Euro has a peculiar and often
fatal habit of stopping to look back after moving off a short
distance.

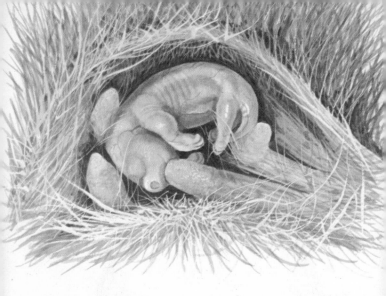

Close-up of a newborn kangaroo in the pouch. The end of the nipple has swollen within the young animal's mouth thus attaching it permanently for the first part of its life.

Reproduction and development in marsupials

In all marsupials the young are born in a very immature state with no eyes or ears and hindlimbs existing only as buds of flesh. Nevertheless certain parts of this tiny young, which has only been developing inside the mother for less than a month, are astonishingly well developed. The fore-paws already have claws and the advanced muscular and nervous development of the front half of the body allows the young to crawl completely unaided from the vaginal opening into the pouch – a distance which usually exceeds six inches depending on the species concerned. This amazing feat is carried out by a creature of tiny size relative to its mother, the newborn kangaroo being less than two inches long and weighing about the same as a newborn mouse! As soon as it gets into the pouch it starts sucking on a nipple. Once inside the mouth cavity, the terminal end of the nipple swells and the young is permanently attached for the first part of its pouch life.

138

The young kangaroo still spends part of the time in the pouch even when it is quite large.

The speed of development in the pouch depends largely on the size of the animal at emergence. For example, the eyes of a Brush-tailed Possum are just beginning to open at about 90 days, the native cat at about 75 days and the Quokka at about 105 days. The young leave the pouch gradually, first venturing out for only short periods and then for longer and longer periods. In the kangaroos there is often a period when the young is outside the pouch permanently but still sticking its head into the pouch cavity to suckle.

A fascinating aspect of marsupial reproduction, particularly in kangaroos and wallabies, is <u>the phenomenon of delayed implantation.</u> This was first investigated in detail for the Quokka. Immediately after a young one is born, the female mates again and another egg is fertilized and starts developing inside the reproductive tract. However, as long as the first young is suckling on the teat, this embryo puts the brakes on, so to speak, and stays floating free inside the reproductive tract with only part of its growth completed. Once the young stops suckling or if it is lost accidentally from the pouch, the development of the new embryo continues where it left off, a full pregnancy is completed and the young is eventually born long after fertilization took place. Before this phenomenon was fully understood it was the cause of some consternation in zoos with captive kangaroos, because it seemed as though young were being born without mating taking place beforehand.

Leadbeater's Possum

The rediscovered marsupials

Just recently there have been three cases of species of possum which were thought to be completely extinct having been rediscovered alive in rather astonishing circumstances.

The Scaly-tailed Possum (*Wyulda squamicaudata*) is a very rare species which up to 1942 had only been known to zoologists from two specimens collected in the very rugged upland regions of the Kimberley district of northern Western Australia. An interesting animal, its name describes its most peculiar feature which is its naked and scaly tail. Recent work by some dedicated naturalists has shown that the species is in fact still extant in this area. It apparently lives in rock piles during the day and feeds at night on tree blossoms.

Leadbeater's Possum (*Gymnobelideus leadbeateri*) is a very rare and beautiful possum which was only found in the early part of the century in the south Gippsland area of Victoria. To the astonishment of many zoologists this species has recently been rediscovered, not in the hidden recesses of some dense and remote habitat, but actually living in dense forests within seventy miles of Melbourne. It is nocturnal, insectivorous and very small, and thus difficult to find, so that its remaining there undiscovered was probably due to its small size and unobtrusive habits.

Finally, a report has recently been published in a most reputable scientific journal of the discovery in a ski hut in the Australian Alps of a tiny live possum-like creature which seems by all its external features to be a living representative of a species previously only described from fossils, called *Burramys parvus*. If this identification proves correct it is a really fascinating discovery because the species is a very primitive form and throws light on the interrelationships of many of the early forms of Australian marsupials. Unfortunately the final definite identification cannot be made until the animal dies and its skull can be observed, and at the time of writing the tiny mystery animal is still alive.

Scaly-tailed Possum

Burramys parvus

Dingo

OTHER MAMMALS, AND INTRODUCED ANIMALS

The Dingo

The name Dingo was a misnomer because it was the rather contemptuous name applied by the aborigines to the white man's dogs and was misinterpreted to mean the animal which the aborigine really called the Warrigal. Although it was once thought to be a separate species, the Dingo is now considered to be of the same species as the Domestic Dog (*Canis familiaris*). It was almost certainly brought into Australia when the aborigines arrived thousands of years ago, but it never spread to Tasmania or to Kangaroo Island off South Australia. The Dingo has become involved in another modern controversy surrounding the origins of the Domestic Dog – whether the basic stock of present dogs arose from a wolf-like or a jackal-like animal. The Dingo is of the wolf type.

The characteristic colour of the Dingo is a pale tawny yellow, but the colour is very variable. It would seem that as Dingoes freely interbreed with Domestic Dogs on farms and stations, there are very few areas of Australia where a 'pure' Dingo strain remains. Dingoes live in small family groups of a dog, a bitch, and her yearling pups. Two features distinguish the Dingo from most Domestic Dogs, its inability to bark (it

Dingoes hang around aborigine camps to scavenge scraps.

howls instead with great gusto) and the fact that its ears stay erect and cannot flop down. Dingoes feed on rabbits, wallabies, rats and reptiles, and kill domestic stock, particularly sheep. For this reason they are regarded as pests and are trapped, baited and shot by government departments of vermin control. In certain areas, such as the west part of the New South Wales-Queensland border, Dingo-proof fences are maintained to keep these animals out of the denser sheep-raising areas. Despite control measures and predation on pups by eagles and snakes, the Dingo holds its own, particularly in some mountainous areas in the less settled parts of the inland. There is evidence that the Dingoes make long migrations from these areas into the more settled agricultural belts.

The Rabbit

The tale of the European Rabbit (*Oryctolagus cuniculus*) in Australia is a truly amazing one. It starts with the astonishing fact that between 1788 and 1859 repeated attempts made by the misguided colonists to introduce the species into Australia always failed, apparently because domesticated strains were always used. However, in 1859 a group of wild rabbits escaped from a pen in Geelong, Victoria, and from that time onwards the numbers and spread of the rabbit population were astronomical. The rabbits were first seen in Queensland in 1886 and reached Fowlers Bay in South Australia in 1891. By 1907 the advance guard had reached Geraldton on the west coast of Western Australia, having advanced over 1,100 miles through Western Australia in sixteen years. Although this spread carried the rabbit in some cases so far into the desert that the onset of drought caused the range to shrink a little, by the early 1900s the rabbit was successfully established over the greater part of Australia.

Once established it built up to fantastic numbers, and in combination with the considerable over-stocking of sheep which occurred at the beginning of the century, the rabbit had a lasting and greatly detrimental effect on the vegetation. It completely destroyed many food grasses in some areas and lowered wool production in particular in many others. The depredations of the rabbits also caused the numbers of many smaller marsupials, that fed on similar grasses and shrubs, to drop considerably and undoubtedly resulted in the extinction

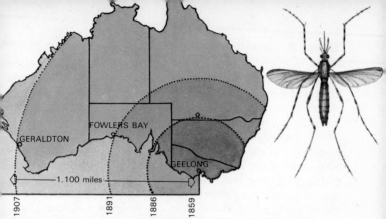

GERALDTON
FOWLERS BAY
GEELONG

1,100 miles

1907 1891 1886 1859

This map shows the amazingly rapid spread of the European Rabbit.
(*Right*) Mosquitoes carry the *Myxoma* virus which has greatly
reduced the European Rabbit population.

of some native species. Between the two world wars and
especially during the second, the number of rabbits became
Australia's major agricultural problem.

Fortunately, as the result of research by a team of zoologists
and virologists, a biological solution was found to this
widespread pest problem. A South American species of
rabbit was found to carry a virus called *Myxoma* which
although only mildly infective in the host species, is fatal to
the wild rabbit. Preliminary trials in the laboratory and field
showed that this virus was transmitted to wild rabbits mainly
by the bite of several species of mosquito. Because of
various factors, field trials carried out during the Second
World War were not at all successful. However, the work
continued and between 1950 and 1953 came a period of
amazing success. Because conditions were ideal for the
mosquitoes to spread and carry the virus, it was disseminated
with tremendous rapidity and some hundreds of millions of
rabbits died of myxomatosis in these years, reducing the
rabbit population to a minute fraction of its former numbers
and actually eradicating it in many areas. The rabbit is now
in numbers which can be controlled by more conventional
means, and the recent tendency of the rabbits to build up a
resistance to the virus now means these methods must be
continually employed

145

Other Australian introductions

The white settlers who arrived to colonize Australia brought with them many household pets, and they also deliberately liberated wild species found in Great Britain for purposes of 'sporting' activities. Although some of these, such as the dog, have largely remained closely associated with man and his dwellings, others have taken to the bush and become very successful living as feral species. For example over considerable areas of the Australian bush are found feral cats which, judging by their well fed and sleek appearance, are making a very good living under wild conditions. Originally introduced for hunting, Foxes are now extremely widespread and have probably been so successful because of their ability to utilize almost any variety of food source. For example, on the Ninety Mile Beach in the north-west of Western Australia – a particularly barren area with little natural food for the fox – these hardy animals scavenge for carcasses washed up by the sea and manage to survive by eating the tiny sand insects and even chewing seaweed. Smaller introduced animals include those that have followed man wherever he has gone, the Brown and Black Rats and the Common Mouse, and these species are now common in the bush. Many birds have also been introduced, including the House Sparrow, which is now found over much of eastern and southern Australia. Other introduced birds include the Tree Sparrow, the Indian Mynah, which has become especially common in and around Melbourne, and several finches. The English

Fox

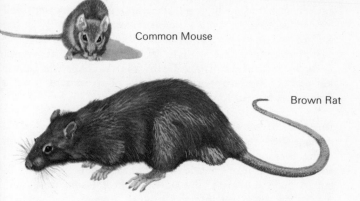

Common Mouse

Brown Rat

Starling is abundant in cities and in the country. It has prospered so well as to become quite a problem. It frequently pillages soft fruit and seedlings, and it competes with native species for nesting space. Blackbirds, Song Thrushes, Indian Turtledoves and others have been introduced. It seems amazing in retrospect that settlers should have found it necessary to import birds to a continent with such a rich bird life of its own. A number of other animals have been introduced or liberated but have not been very successful and so are limited to small areas. These include horses, donkeys, wild pigs and camels.

It is thought that many of the more common introduced species (especially the Fox and the cat) competed with or preyed upon many of the smaller forms of marsupials and as a result the stock of the original inhabitants has been severly reduced and many species have become extinct.

Native Australian non-marsupial mammals

As well as the Dingo which was probably brought in by the aborigines, there is one other group of mammals which have recently arrived in Australia. These are certain species of rodent which, from their distribution, almost certainly arrived over the land bridge from Asia. Another group, the bats, have probably been in Australia for millions of years.

The Beaver Rat or Water Rat (*Hydromys chrysogaster*) shows several interesting adaptations to a semi-aquatic existence including high-set eyes, and nostrils located well forward so that the animal presents a very low profile on the surface of the water. It also has thick, seal-like fur and partially webbed feet. It lives in streams and swamps and feeds on mussels, snails and freshwater crayfish. The Beaver Rat makes long burrows in the banks of streams. It is not a pest but is hunted for its fine pelt.

The cane fields of Queensland are a favourite habitat of the Dusky Field Rat (*Rattus conatus*), and it causes considerable damage there to the cane. A carrier of a protozoan infection, which is transmitted to man, it is because of this species that the cane is burnt in order to drive out the rats before it can be cut. A good burrower, the Dusky Field Rat sometimes goes more than three feet into the ground. It feeds on stems and leaves of grasses and occasionally eats smaller rodents.

The Eastern Pseudo-rat (*Pseudomys australis*) is a species of higher altitudes living in mountainous valleys and also in

Dusky Field Rat

Beaver Rat

Eastern Pseudo-rat

Little Brown Bat

Gould's Fruit Bat

beech and pine scrub. It is fairly rare and like other species in the group has a rather localized distribution.

Gould's Fruit Bat (*Pteropus gouldii*) is a representative of the fruit bats or flying foxes, which are large fruit and blossom eaters living in camps of many individuals. They are quite noisy animals and can be heard squabbling among themselves as they roost. They locate their food mainly by smell, and often attack orchards on damp, still nights when scent travels long distances. Gould's Fruit Bat is a widespread species found in mangrove swamps all over the northern regions of Australia.

The second group of bats, the smaller insectivorous ones, are widely distributed and represented by a number of species in Australia. They tend to live in small colonies in caves or holes and cracks in trees and consume many night-flying insects. The Little Brown Bat (*Vespadelus pumilus*) is quite common all over the continent and is often found under the bark of trees.

Fallow Deer

European Hedgehog

Introductions into New Zealand

New Zealand has only two native mammals, the Long-tailed Bat, also found in Australia, and the New Zealand Short-tailed Bat. Compared with the many European species introduced into Australia, the number of different species liberated in New Zealand over the last hundred years is absolutely astonishing. The list given here is incomplete and yet shows the great diversity of species brought from every continent. Those mammals starred on the list are those that have established themselves on a permanent basis, although some have only a limited distribution. Introduced species make up most of New Zealand's present bird population.

The Brush-tailed Possum (*Trichosurus vulpecula*) was liberated from Australia at the turn of the century and spread to become a major problem due to the damage it has done to native and exotic forests and to orchards and gardens. Although trapped for their skins, they do damage far outweighing any value from the skin trade. The European Hedgehog (*Erinaceus europaeus*) is widespread in considerable numbers, and although it benefits farmers and gardeners as it destroys insect pests, its habit of eating the eggs of ground nesting birds is detrimental to the native birds. Birds, small game and poultry are also extensively preyed on by the Stoat (*Mustela erminea*) and the European Polecat or Ferret (*Mustela putorius*). Wild Goats (*Capra hircus*) and the many forms of deer (especially the Red Deer, *Cervus elaphus*) are very destructive of the native vegetation, in particular that found in sub-alpine and alpine regions, and this in turn causes great problems of erosion. All in all the introduced animals of New Zealand have left the country with an enormous economic and ecological problem, and indeed the introduction of many of these species has resulted in irreversible changes in the native flora and fauna.

BANDICOOTS
BRUSH-TAILED POSSUM*
SCRUB WALLABY*
SWAMP WALLABY*
TAMMAR*
ROCK WALLABY*
KANGAROOS
EURO
POTOROO
HEDGEHOG*
RACCOON
STOAT*
FERRET*
WEASEL*
CAT*
CHIPMUNK
BLACK RAT*
BROWN RAT*
HOUSE MOUSE*
GUINEA PIG
RABBIT*
HARE*
GOAT*
HIMALAYAN TAHR*
CHAMOIS*
WILDEBEEST
RED DEER*
AXIS DEER*
SAMBAR DEER*
WAPITI*
JAPANESE DEER*
FALLOW DEER*
WHITE-TAILED DEER*
MULE DEER

MOOSE*
WILD PIG*
ALPACA
LLAMA
WILD HORSE*
ZEBRA

BLACK SWAN
BROWN QUAIL
ROSELLA
KOOKABURRA
MAGPIE
BROWN OWL
MALLARD
PHEASANT
SKYLARK
SONG THRUSH
BLACKBIRD
HEDGE SPARROW
ROOK
STARLING
HOUSE SPARROW
CHAFFINCH
REDPOLL
GOLDFINCH
GREENFINCH
YELLOW BUNTING
CANADA GOOSE
CALIFORNIA QUAIL
VIRGINIAN QUAIL
CHUKAR
LACENECK DOVE
INDIAN MYNAH
PEAFOWL

151

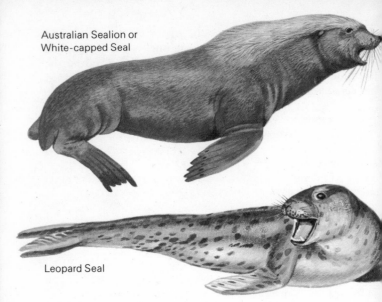

Australian Sealion or
White-capped Seal

Leopard Seal

Seals and sealions

Seals are divided into two main groups, the earless seals
which actually have ears but no external ear lobes, and the
eared seals which have prominent ear lobes. The first group
have their hind feet permanently directed backwards and,
although very well adapted for moving in the water, can only
just move around on land. The second group can swing their
hind flippers forward and thus are much more active on land.
Many of the forms of seal found on Australian coasts are
really only visitors from the waters much farther south and,
as in other parts of the world, the excessive exploitation of
seals has reduced the numbers of the coastal forms to the
point where many are verging on extinction.

The Australian Fur Seal (*Arctocephalus doriferus*) once used
to be reported in large herds but is now much reduced. Like
many other eared seals, the males form harems during the
breeding season and lord it over groups of females on the
beaches where birth and mating take place.

The Australian Sealion or White-capped Seal (*Neophoca
cinerea*) is the largest eared seal in Australian waters and has

a very attractive mane of coarse yellow hair. Unlike many other seals, this species does not migrate but remains with a close attachment to smallish coastal areas. It does not fast as do other seals, and feeds continually throughout the year, being especially fond of eating penguins.

The Leopard Seal (*Hydrurga leptonyx*) is an Antarctic species which occurs as an occasional straggler on Australian and New Zealand coasts. It is a very efficient predator and eats great numbers of penguins and the young of other seal species.

The Southern Elephant Seal (*Mirounga leonina*) was once very common on Australian coasts but now only survives on Macquarie Island and other islands in the Antarctic Ocean. The males are very large and have an inflatable trunk which dilates when they are fighting with each other.

The Dugong or Sea Cow

This species actually occurs from the Red Sea through the Indian ocean to northern Australia, but it survives in any numbers only in waters of northern Australia. The Dugong

Australian Fur Seal

Elephant Seal

(*Dugong dugon*) is a member of a very small but fascinating order of mammals, the Sirenia, which includes also the manatees of North and South America, the West Indies and West Africa. Very large slow moving aquatic animals, they make greater use of their flippers than do the whales and the mother actually clasps her young to her belly while feeding it and will guide the infant's head to the surface when it rises to breathe. It is thought that this habit and the creature's odd-shaped head may have given rise to the old sailors' yarn of the mermaid. Dugongs are supposed to be rather closely related to elephants as their teeth are very similar to those of elephants.

Dugongs are found in shallow bays and estuaries where they feed slowly on huge beds of marine grasses. These they pull off with their prehensile, thick upper lip. The males have small tusks which they use to root up the grasses and to obtain shellfish. Dugongs are very social animals and slow movers, so that they are easily hunted. As they provide great quantities of blubber, oil and tusks, their numbers have been severely depleted and they are now absent from many

It is quite likely that the Dugong gave rise to stories of mermaids.

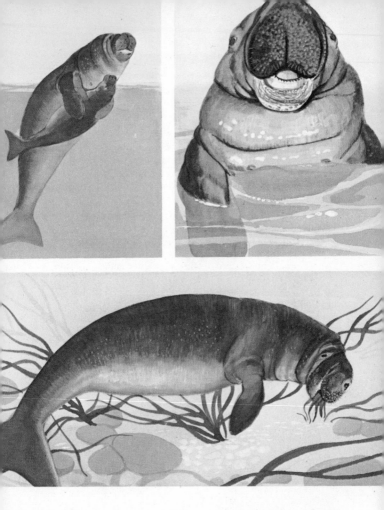

parts of their former range. They are potentially a great source of domestic food as the meat is excellent, and they are the only marine mammal which feeds on marine grasses. Dugongs thus utilize food which is otherwise completely untouched by man or by any animal eaten by him. Some biologists have thus suggested that the species should be domesticated as a source of meat.

BOOKS TO READ

For general introductions to the animal life of this region, the following books are recommended and should be available through public libraries and bookshops.

Animals of the World: Australia. Hamlyn, London, 1968.

Australian Spiders by K. C. McKeown. Angus and Robertson, Sydney, 1963.

Birds of Western Australia (4th edition) by D. L. Serventy and H. M. Whittell. Lamb Publications, Perth, 1967.

Birds of the World by O. L. Austin. Hamlyn, London, 1962.

Furred Animals of Australia (8th edition) by E. Troughton. Angus and Robertson, Sydney, 1965.

Introduced Mammals of New Zealand by K. A. Wodzicki. New Zealand Government Printer.

Living Birds of the World by E. T. Gilliard. Hamish Hamilton, London, 1958.

The Mammals by Desmond Morris. Hodder and Stoughton, London, 1965.

Reptiles of Australia by Eric Worrell. Angus and Robertson, Sydney, 1963.

Snakes of Australia (Revised edition) by J. R. Kinghorn. Angus and Robertson, Sydney, 1964.

What Bird Is That ? A Guide to the Birds of Australia (4th edition) by N. W. Cayley. Angus and Robertson, Sydney, 1966.

The interested reader is also strongly recommended to look at the journals of the various naturalist clubs, especially the *West Australian Naturalist* and the *Victorian Naturalist*, the journal of the Australian Museum *Australian Natural History*, and the main Australian ornithological journal *Emu*.

INDEX

Page numbers in bold type refer to illustrations.

SOME OTHER TITLES IN THIS SERIES